A FATHER'S CARE

BIBLE TRUTHS

1

Third Edition

BJU PRESS
Greenville, South Carolina

This textbook was written by members of the faculty and staff of Bob Jones University. Standing for the "old-time religion" and the absolute authority of the Bible since 1927, Bob Jones University is the world's leading fundamental Christian university. The staff of the University is devoted to educating Christian men and women to be servants of Jesus Christ in all walks of life.

Providing unparalleled academic excellence, Bob Jones University prepares its students through its offering of over 120 majors, while its fervent spiritual emphasis prepares their minds and hearts for service and devotion to the Lord Jesus Christ.

Consultants
from the administration, faculty, and staff of Bob Jones University
Philip D. Smith, Ed.D., *Provost*
James R. Davis, M.A., *Director of Product Development, Bob Jones University Press*
Dorothy Buckley, *Elementary Authors Coordinator, Bob Jones University Press*
Coart Ramey, M.A., *Secondary Authors, Bob Jones University Press*
Bryan Smith, M.A., *Secondary Authors, Bob Jones University Press*
Ann Larson, M.A., *Grade 1 Consultant, Bob Jones University Press*

NOTE:
The fact that materials produced by other publishers may be referred to in this volume does not constitute an endorsement of the content or theological position of materials produced by such publishers. Any references and ancillary materials are listed as an aid to the student or the teacher and in an attempt to maintain the accepted academic standards of the publishing industry.

Bible Truths 1
A Father's Care Third Edition

Coordinating Writer
Tammie D. Jacobs

Writers
Peggy S. Alier
Ann Larson
Robin Holte Scroggins
Robin Sisney Wood

Designer
Wendy Searles

Project Coordinator
Richard Ayers

Computer Formatting
Peggy Hargis

Project Editors
Catherine Anderson
Nathan Huffstutler

Photo Acquisition
Tara Swaney
Joyce Landis

Photograph credits appear on page 240.

Printed in the United States of America

ISBN 978-1-59166-970-8

15 14 13 12 11 10 9 8 7 6 5 4 3 2 1

Table of Contents

From Nothing
Genesis 1:1

Name ______________________

Circle *yes* or *no* for each sentence.

1. God has always been. yes no
2. God lives forever. yes no
3. Man helped God make the world. yes no
4. God made the world from nothing. yes no
5. God spoke the world into being. yes no

Color all the pictures that finish the sentence.

I am thankful God made _____.

Day 1: Day and Night
Genesis 1:2-5

Name ________________________________

Circle the three correct words to finish the sentence.

1. Before God made light, the earth was _____.

light	dark	empty
full	without shape	round

Draw a line to finish each sentence.

2. God called the light _____. — night

3. God called the darkness _____. — day

Circle the things you do in the day with 
yellow
.

Circle the things you do at night with 
blue
.

Day 2: Sky and Water

Genesis 1:6-8

Name ____________________

God divided the sky from the earth.

Draw a  or  in the box to finish each sentence.

1. The sky had water in the ☐.
2. The earth was covered with ☐.

Hidden in the clouds are things you might find in the sky.
Color the five pictures hidden in the clouds.

Day 3: Land, Seas, and Plants

Genesis 1:9-13

Name ______________________________

Use the words in the word bank to finish the sentences.

plants
seas
trees

1. God moved the ________________ to make the dry land.

2. God covered the land with ________________ and ________________.

Draw waves in the water.

Draw trees, grass, and flowers on the land.

Color your picture of God's creation.

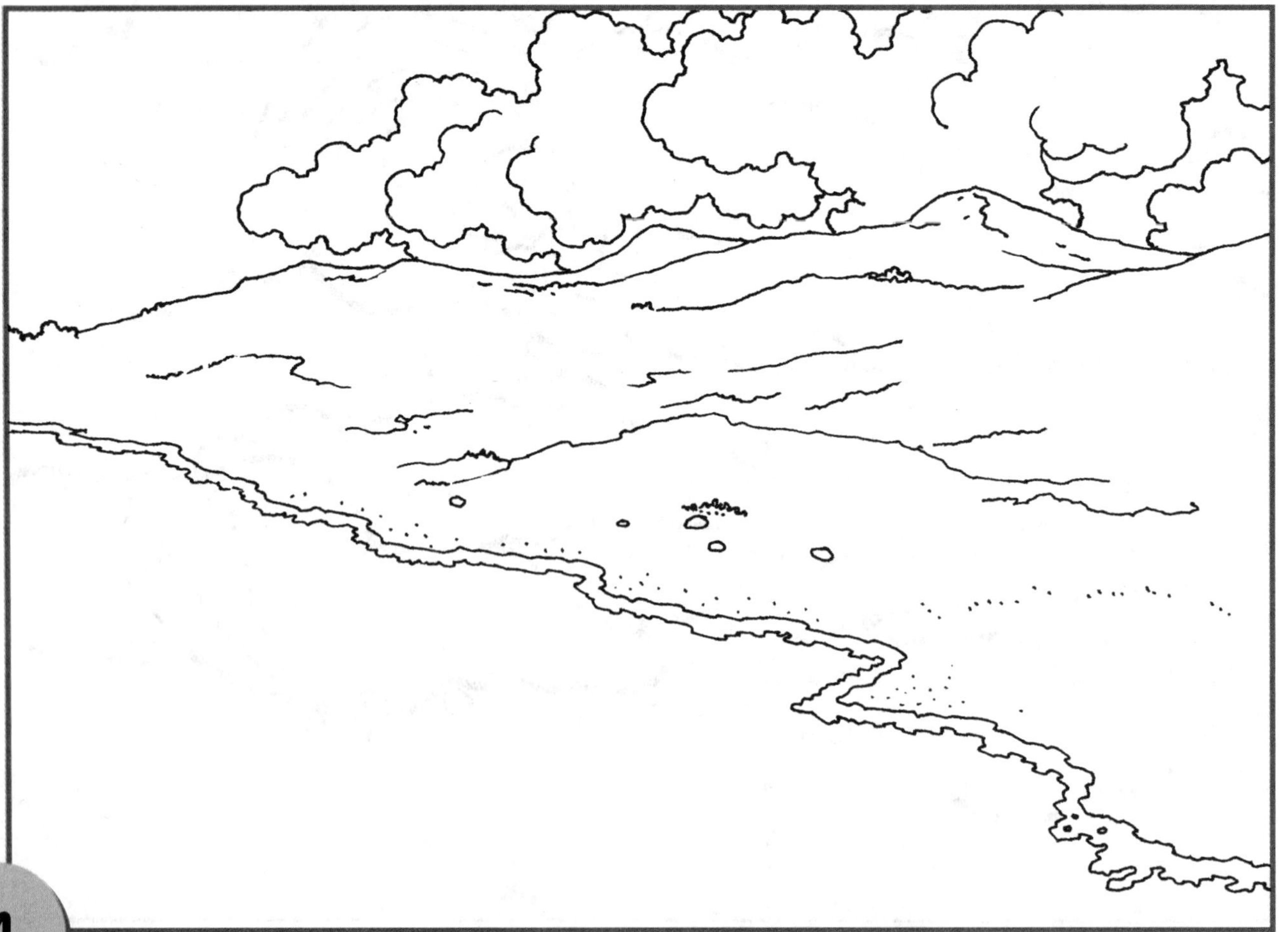

Day 4: Sun, Moon, and Stars
Genesis 1:14-19

Name ______________________________

Draw one line to the light God made for the day.

Draw two lines to the lights God made for the night.

Circle the lights made by God.
Make an *X* on the lights made by man.

Day 5: Fish and Birds

Genesis 1:20-23

Name ______________________

Use the words in the word bank to finish the sentences.

birds
fish

1. God made ______________ for the water.

2. God made ______________ for the sky.

Learn to draw a fish. Trace the dotted lines. Make an eye.

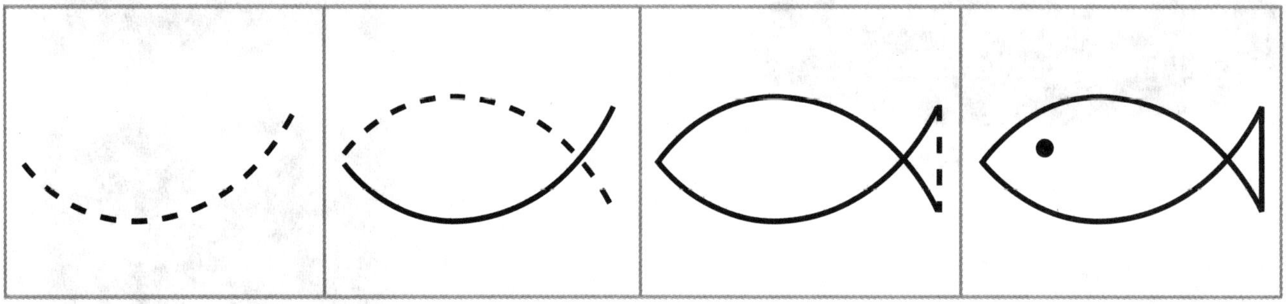

Draw fish in the water. Color your fish.

Day 6: Man and Animals
Genesis 1:24-31; 2:7

Name ______________________

God made the land creatures.

God made each kind of animal different from the others.

Draw a line to match each animal with a baby of its kind.

Man was made in the image of God.

God gave man a soul that would live forever.

God made man to love and serve Him.

Answer the questions.

1. Who made you? ______________

2. Did God make all that man and animals need? ______________

Remember to thank God for supplying your needs.

The God of Order

Name ______________________________

God is a God of order.

The sun was made after God made the sky. The plants were created after God made the land for them to grow. The animals were created after God made places for them to live.

Complete the sentence.

God is a God of _______________.

Write the number of each day of God's Creation.

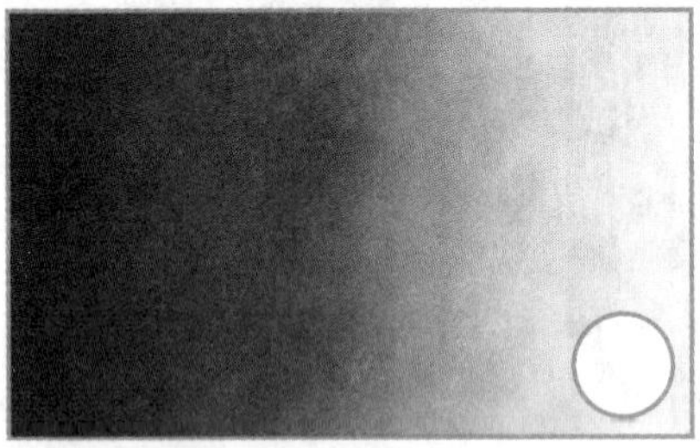

Take a closer look!

Point at each day as the sentences are read.

On Day 4, God added to what He made on Day 1.

On Day 5, God added to what He made on Day 2.

On Day 6, God added to what He made on Day 3.

Day 7: God Rested
Genesis 2:1-2

Name ____________________

God created all things in six days.
God rested on the seventh day.

Answer the question.

God wants us to be like Him.

1. What should I do one day each week?

____

May

Sunday	Monday	Tuesday	Wednesday	Thursday	Friday	Saturday
				1	2	3
4	5	6	7	8	9	10
11	12	13	14	15	16	17
18	19	20	21	22	23	24
25	26	27	28	29	30	31

Fill in the circle next to the correct answer.

2. How many days are in each week?

○ five ○ six ○ seven

3. What is the first day of the week?

○ Sunday ○ Monday ○ Tuesday

The Lord's Day
Genesis 2:3

Name ____________________

God made one day different from the others.
We call this day the Lord's Day.

When Jesus died, He rose on the first day of the week.
Christians worship on Sunday, the first day of the week.

Color the puzzle.

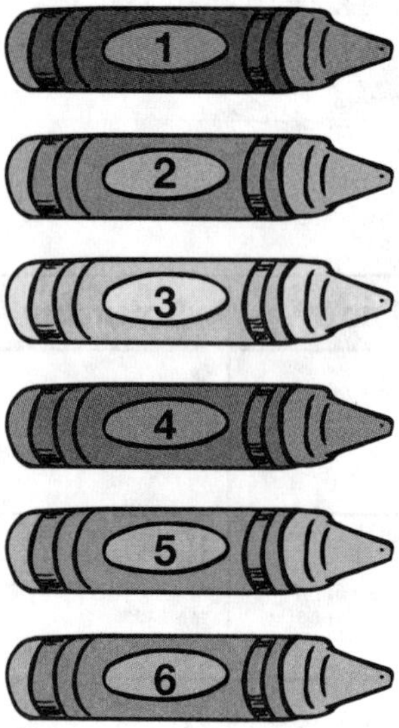

1
2
3
4
5
6

Finish the sentence.

On the Lord's Day, my family ____________________
____.

Disobeying God

Genesis 2:15–3:6

Name ______________________

God made Adam and Eve to obey Him.
Eve listened to Satan and disobeyed God.
Adam listened to Eve and disobeyed God.
The Bible says it is sin to disobey.

Number the pictures in story order.

How can I know what God says?
The Bible is the Word of God.

Circle all the answers that finish the sentence for you.

I can learn God's Word by _____.

Sinful Traps

Name ______________________________

Traps are used to capture animals.
An animal in a trap cannot get out alone.

Sin is like a trap.
People in sin cannot get out alone.

God wants to forgive sin.
Forgiveness sets people free from sin.

Make an *X* on each sin which may trap you.

being selfish

obeying parents

complaining

helping

kind words

lying

not obeying

telling the truth

taking things

God forgives all sin.

When you are tempted, pray for God's help.

When you sin, ask God for forgiveness.

Hiding from God

Genesis 3:7-19, 23-24

Name ______________________

Write *me* on each blank. Read the sentences.

Adam and Eve hid from God when they sinned.

God sees everything.
God saw Adam and Eve when they sinned.

1. God sees ______________ when I sin.

God punished Adam and Eve for their sin.

2. God will punish ______________ for my sin.

Color the happy face or the sad face to finish each sentence.

1. God is _____ when I obey my parents.	☺ ☹
2. God is _____ when I obey Him.	☺ ☹
3. God is _____ when I hide my sin.	☺ ☹
4. God is _____ when I confess my sin.	☺ ☹

Reading from the Bible
Table of Contents

Name ____________________

BIBLE STUDY SKILLS

You can find verses about Creation in your Bible. Creation verses are in Genesis. Verses about Adam and Eve disobeying God are in Genesis.

Learn it!

Learn to use the table of contents in your Bible.

- The table of contents is in the front of your Bible.
- Genesis is at the top of the list.
- Look for the page number.

Books of the Old Testament

	Page
Genesis	1
Exodus	32
Leviticus	59
Numbers	77
Deuteronomy	106
Joshua	128
Judges	144
Ruth	160

Practice it!

Use the table of contents in your Bible to find the answer.

1. What is the page number of Genesis in your Bible? ____________________

2. Turn to the first page of Genesis. Did you find it? ____________________

God's Protection

Name ______________________________

God gave animals protection against their enemies.

Draw a line to connect the animal with the protection God gave it.

God cares for me.
God promises to protect me.

Fill in the circle next to the ending that shows trust in God's protection.

Jamie saw the rain pour and the lightning flash outside the car.

Jamie should _____.

- ○ pray for Daddy that he might drive safely home
- ○ cry for Daddy to stop the car

Salvation from God

John 3:16-17

Name ______________________

Use the words in the word bank to finish the sentences. Write the words in the puzzle.

God	saved
Son	world

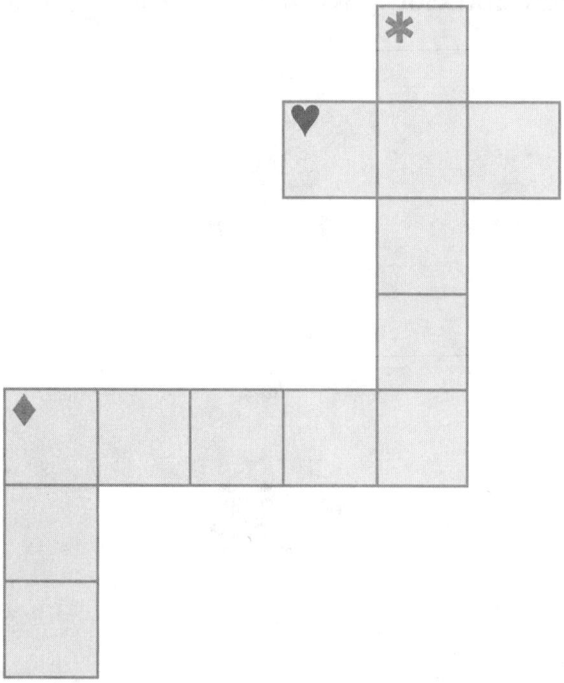

Across

♥ Eternal life means life with ____ forever.

♦ Through Jesus the people of the world can be ____.

Down

✱ God sent Jesus into the ____.

♦ Jesus is the only ____ of God.

Color each space with a dot yellow.

Color the other spaces blue.

Read the truth about God.

God loves me

God's Promised Plan

Name ____________________

God promised to send a Savior for sin.
God sent Jesus to die for the sin of all people.
God wants everyone to accept His gift.

God promised the Savior for sin. 1

1. **Cut the pictures apart.**
2. **Put the pictures in order and staple at the top to make a book.**
3. **Use your book to tell someone that Jesus is the Savior.**

God promised the Savior for sin. 1

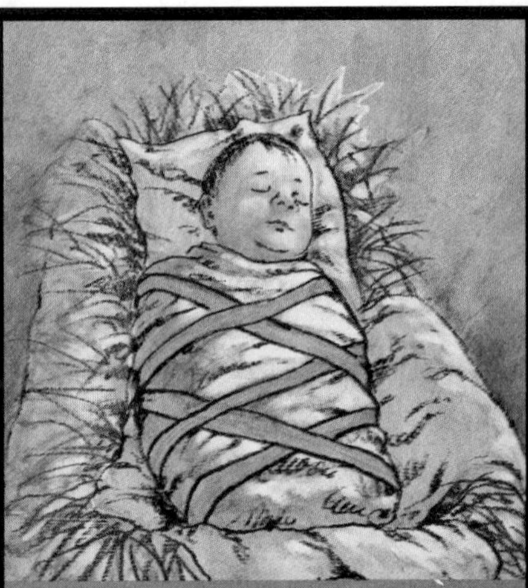

God sent Jesus. 2

Jesus died for our sin. 3

Jesus rose again. 4

Jesus is the Savior. 5

Is Jesus your Savior? 6

God's Promised Plan (continued)

I Corinthians 15:3	I John 4:14	I Corinthians 15:21-22
John 3:16	Acts 5:30-31	I Corinthians 15:4

The Shepherd

John 10:14-17; Psalm 23:1-3

Name ______________________

Sheep need a shepherd to keep them safe.

In the Bible, God calls people sheep.
Jesus is the Shepherd. He rescues people
from sin.

People need Jesus to guide them
in the way they should go.

Help each sheep find help from its shepherd.

Draw a line from each sheep to the shepherd with the opposite action.

hating
giving
hurting
telling the truth
taking
loving
lying
helping

For All People

Romans 5:12;
I Corinthians 15:22

Name ______________________

Use the words in the word bank to finish the sentences.

1. God ____________ Adam and loved him.

2. Adam disobeyed ____________.

3. All ____________ came from Adam.

4. Adam's sin is in ____________ people.

people
all
God
made

5. God ____________ all people.

6. God ____________ Jesus to die.

7. ____________ died to give salvation.

8. God's salvation is for ____________ people.

all
Jesus
loves
sent

Noah's Obedience
Genesis 6

Name ______________________________

Noah obeyed God.

Noah built an ark.

Begin at the star. Connect the dots to complete the picture. Color the picture.

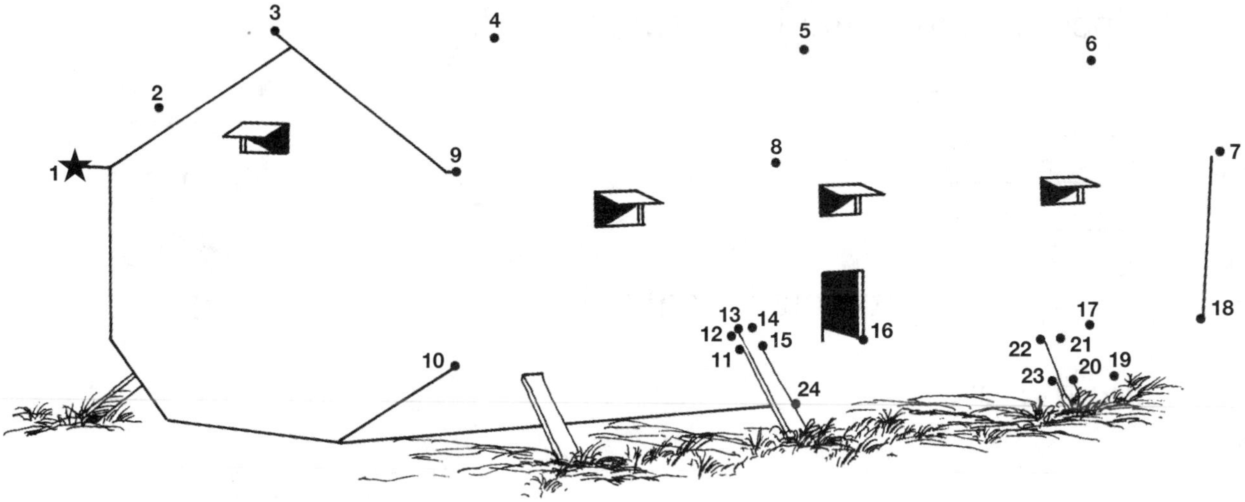

1
2
3
4
5
6
7
8
9
10
11
12
13
14
15
16
17
18
19
20
21
22
23
24

Circle the picture that answers each question.

1. What was God going to use to punish sin?

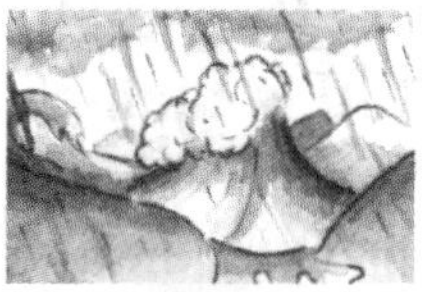

2. What did Noah use to build the ark?

3. What did God tell Noah to take into the ark?

The Flood
Genesis 7

Name ______________________________

Use the words in the word bank to finish the sentences.

1. God shut the door of the ___________.

2. The ______________ fell for forty days and nights.

3. The people and animals outside the ark ______________.

4. ___________ protected Noah's family inside the ark.

Word bank
died
rain
God
ark

Color the puzzle.

1 = 
blue

2 = 
red

The red squares will tell you whether you need to be afraid if God is taking care of you.

1	1	1	1	1	1	1	1	1	1
1	2	1	1	2	1	2	2	2	1
1	2	2	1	2	1	2	1	2	1
1	2	1	2	2	1	2	1	2	1
1	2	1	1	2	1	2	2	2	1
1	1	1	1	1	1	1	1	1	1

God's Promise

Genesis 8–9:19

Name ______________________

Cut out the three small pictures on the right. Glue them in the correct places in the scene. Cut out the finished scene.

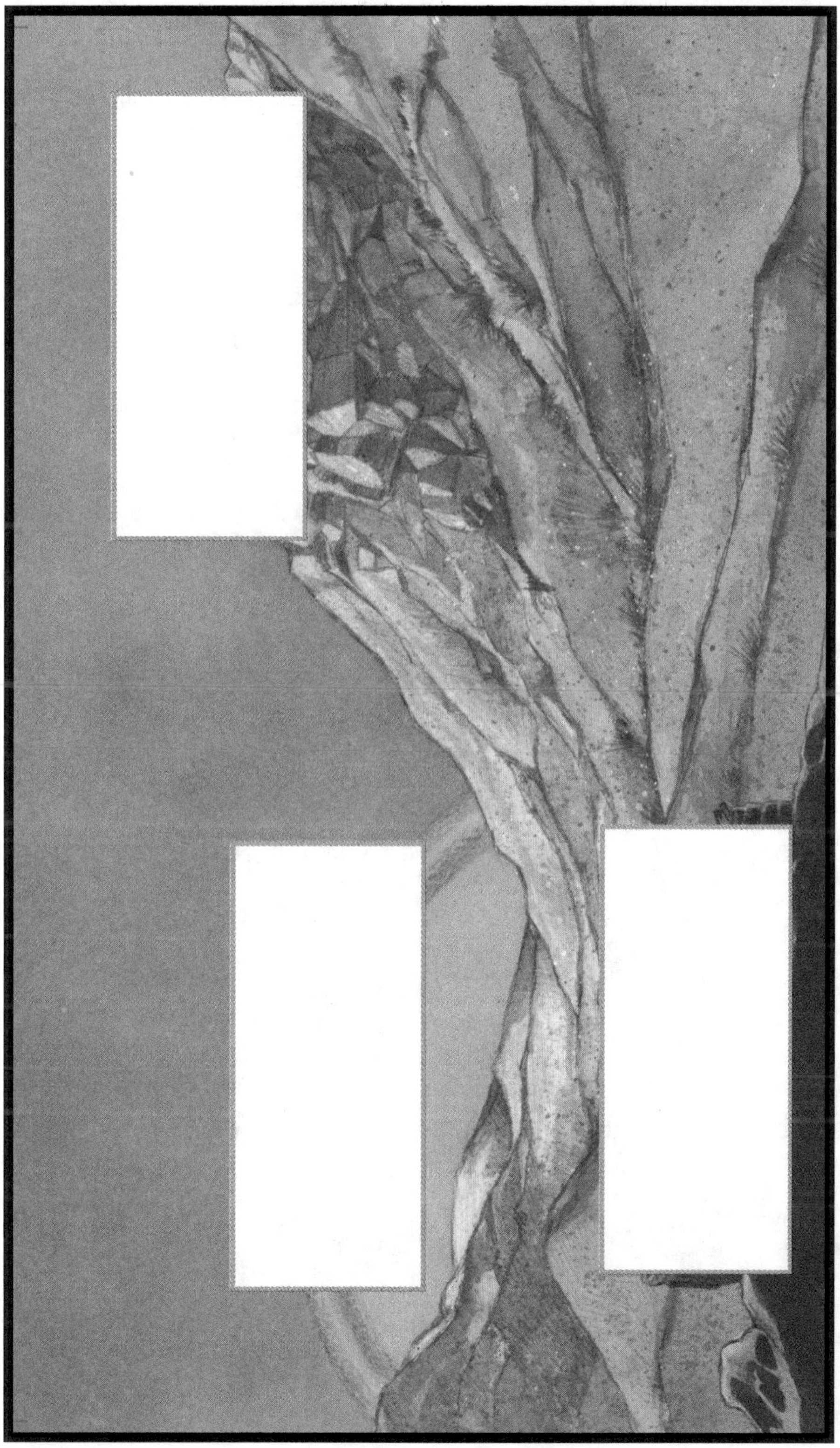

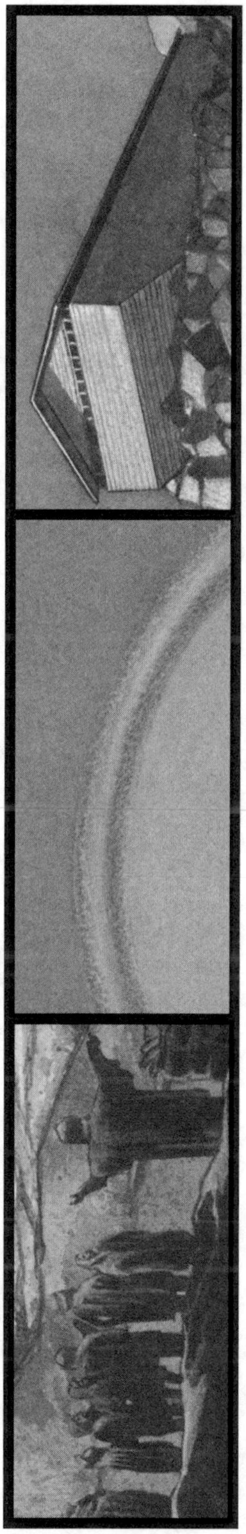

God's Promise (continued)

God's Protection

Name ______________________

Have you ever been afraid?
Will God help you?

God protected Noah's family.
God will protect you.

Read the sentences.
Draw a rainbow next to the correct answer.

1. Julie felt afraid of her dark bedroom.
   Julie should _____.

   ☐ hide under the covers

   ☐ ask God to keep her safe

2. Bobby felt afraid of his friend's big dog.
   Bobby should _____.

   ☐ cry and run away

   ☐ ask God to keep him safe

Reading from the Bible
Table of Contents

Name ______________________

BIBLE STUDY SKILLS

Remember that the table of contents is at the front of your Bible.
The table of contents gives the beginning page number of each book.

Use this table of contents to answer the questions.

1. On what page does Exodus begin?

______

2. What book is before Exodus?

______

3. On what page does Judges begin?

______

4. What book is after Judges?

______

Books of the Old Testament

	Page
Genesis	1
Exodus	32
Leviticus	59
Numbers	77
Deuteronomy	106
Joshua	128
Judges	144
Ruth	160

Use the table of contents in your own Bible to find the page numbers.

Numbers ______

Joshua ______

Abram's Faith

Genesis 11:26–12:9

Name ______________________

God spoke to Abram.
Abram listened.
Abram obeyed.
God blessed Abram.

Fill in the circle next to the correct answer.

1. God asked Abram to _____.
   - ○ move
   - ○ make a tent

2. God promised to give Abram a large _____.
   - ○ mountain
   - ○ family

3. Abram built an _____.
   - ○ altar
   - ○ ark

Color the correct face 
yellow
.

4. When Abram obeyed God, he was _____.

   happy   sad

5. When I obey God, I am _____.

   happy   sad

Finding Joy

Name ______________________

Sad things happen sometimes.
Friends move away.
A pet gets lost.
You get sick.

What can you do to find God's joy when you feel sad?

Read the sentences.
Make an *X* in the *True* column if it is a way to find God's joy.
Make an *X* in the *False* column if it is not a way to find God's joy.

How can I find joy when I am sad?	True	False
I can think about a Bible verse.		
I can slam the door.		
I can sing a song of praise to God.		
I can get mad at my friends.		
I can ask God to help me.		
I can obey my parents.		

Abram's Lie
Genesis 12:10-20

Name ______________________

Abram was scared of Pharaoh.
Abram did not trust in God.
Abram told Pharaoh a lie.

Use the words in the word bank to finish the sentences.

1. Abram and Sarai went to ________________.
2. Sarai was very ________________.
3. Abram did not tell the ________________.
4. Pharaoh made Abram and Sarai leave Egypt when he found out about the ________________.

truth
Egypt
lie
pretty

Abram's lie displeased God.
Abram's lie hurt him.
Abram's lie hurt his family.
Abram's lie hurt Pharaoh.
Abram's lie hurt Pharaoh's family.
It is never right to tell a lie.

The Truth

Name ______________________________

Read the sentences.
Color the face by the correct answer.

Beth threw the ball.
The ball hit the china cup.
The cup broke.
Mom asked Beth about the cup.
Beth said the dog broke the cup.

Did Beth tell Mom the truth?

☺ Yes ☹ No

Tim wanted to play.
Dad said to work for one hour first.
Tim did not work at all. Tim played.
Dad asked Tim about his work.
Tim told Dad he did not work.

Did Tim tell Dad the truth?

☺ Yes ☹ No

Abram's Kindness
Genesis 13

Name ______________________________

Draw a line to match the first part of the sentence with the end of the sentence. Read each complete sentence.

1. The servants were fighting	Abram.
2. Abram let Lot	choose first.
3. God blessed	about the land.

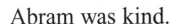

Abram was kind.
Lot was selfish.
How did God bless Abram for his kindness?

Draw a picture of what God gave to Abram and his family.

Selfish or Kind?

Name ______________________________

How do you treat others?
Are you kind?
Are you selfish?

Read the sentences.
Put a ⌒ on the face next to the sentences that show that a person is selfish.
Put a ◡ on the face next to the sentences that show that a person is kind.

1. I want to go first!
2. You may have my cookie.

3. I'm smarter than you are.
4. I don't mind being last.

5. I'm sorry I hurt you.
6. I want to do it my way.

Showing Mercy
Genesis 14

Name ______________________________

Lot was not kind to Abram.
Lot took the best land.
Abram showed mercy to Lot
when Lot needed help.

Circle all of the correct answers.

1. Abram and his servants saved _____.

   Lot   the prisoners   the stolen animals

2. Abram gave a tenth to _____.

   the King of Sodom   Melchizedek

Mercy is showing kindness to
someone who did not earn it.
How can you show mercy to others?

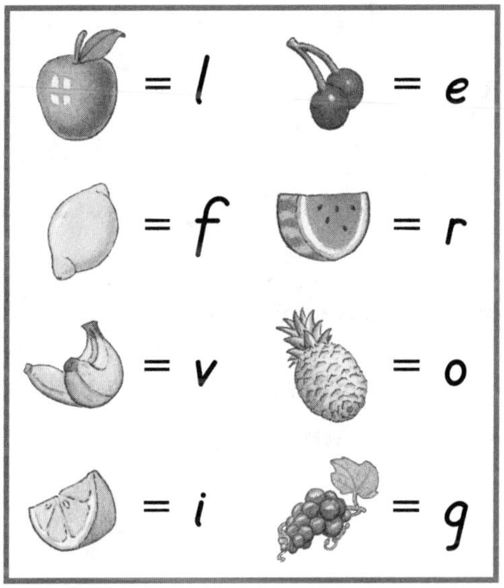

= l
= e
= f
= r
= v
= o
= i
= g

Use the code to find the missing letters.
Write the letters in the correct boxes.

I can  and

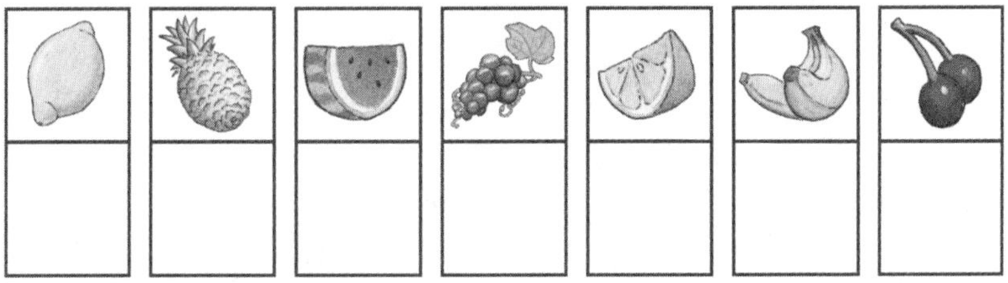 those who hurt me.

God's Plan
Genesis 13:15

Name ______________________

God had a plan for Abram's family.
He promised to bless them.

God has a plan for you.
How can you know God's blessings?

Color the boxes with *O*s 
green
.

Color the boxes with other letters 
yellow
.

Use the word you found to finish the sentence.
Read the sentence.

I can know God's blessings when I

____
_ _ _ _ _ _ _
______________________.

Abraham's Reward

Genesis 17-18; 21:1-7

Name ________________________

Abram waited on God.
Abram waited a long time.
God kept His promise to Abram.
God was not late.

Fill in the circle next to the correct answer.

1. God changed Abram's name to _____.
   ○ Abraham
   ○ Noah

2. One of the men who visited Abraham was _____.
   ○ Lot
   ○ the Lord

3. God gave Abraham and Sarah a _____.
   ○ horse
   ○ son

4. They named their son _____.
   ○ Isaac
   ○ Ben

How old was Abraham when Isaac was born?

Cross out the 3s. Cross out the 4s.
Write the other numbers in order to complete the sentence below.

3	1	4	3	0	3	4	3	0	4

Abraham was _______________ years old!

Abraham's Test

Genesis 22:1-18

Name ________________________________

Abraham loved God.
Abraham loved Isaac.
Whom did Abraham love more?
God gave Abraham a test to find out.

Use the words in the word bank to complete the puzzle.

test	ram	son	altar

Across

1. God provided a _____.

3. God gave Abraham a _____.

Down

2. Abraham laid Isaac on the _____.

4. Isaac was Abraham's _____.

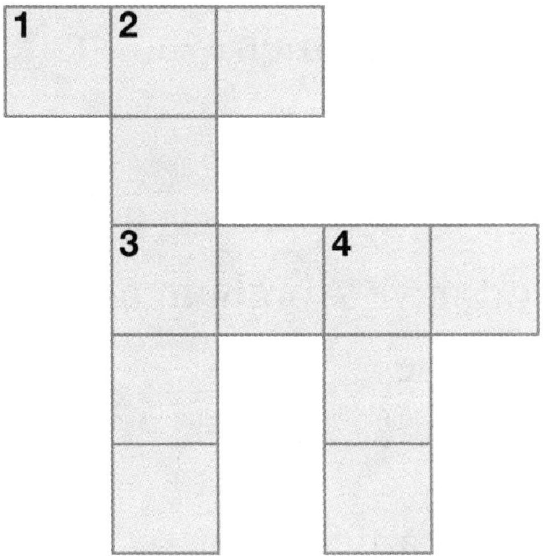
1
2
3
4

Use the words in the word bank to finish the sentences.

1. Abraham obeyed _______________.

2. God promised to _______________ Abraham.

bless
God

I Believe

Romans 4:3

Name ______________________________

Abraham believed in God.
Abraham's belief pleased God.
What do you believe?

HOLY
BIBLE

Color the scrolls that describe what a Christian should believe.

I believe God answers prayer.	I believe I never do wrong.	I believe God created the world.
I believe Jesus died for my sins.	I believe God hates sin.	I believe God loves me.
I believe God is good.	I believe it is okay to tell a lie.	I believe the Bible is true.

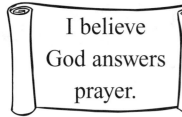

Cross out all the letters found in the word *crayon*.
Write the remaining letters in order in the blank to finish the sentence.

C	B	R	I	A	B	Y	L	O	N	E

A Christian finds out what to believe in the ________________.

Real Obedience

Name ___________________________

Obedience pleases God.
What is obedience?
Obedience is doing what is right.
Are you obedient?

Read each sentence. Make a ✓ next to the sentences that describe what you already do. Circle the sentences that describe things you need to work on.

______ 1. I come to the table when called.

______ 2. I clean up my room.

______ 3. I do my schoolwork.

______ 4. I do not slam the door.

______ 5. I get out of bed on time.

______ 6. I share my toys.

Draw a picture of a time when you obeyed your parents.

God Provides
Genesis 24

Name ______________________________

Abraham wanted a good wife for Isaac.
God provided a wife for Isaac.

Cut out the pictures on the heavy dark lines.
Put the pictures in story order.

God Provides (continued)

Not the Same
Genesis 25:20-34

Name ______________________

God gave Isaac and Rebekah twin boys.

Not all twins look the same.
Not all twins act the same.

God makes every person different.
God made Jacob and Esau different.

Make an *X* under the name of the person described.

	Jacob	Esau
He was born first.		
He was red and hairy.		
He stayed home among the tents.		
He liked to hunt.		
His mother loved him more.		
His father loved him more.		

God's Care
Genesis 26:1-11

Name ______________________________

Circle the best word to finish the sentence.

1. There was not any ______ or water in the land.

trees food

2. God told ______ to take his family and follow Him.

Jacob Isaac

3. Isaac ______ God.

obeyed disobeyed

God led Isaac to food and water.
God promised Isaac the same land God
had promised Abraham.

Make an *X* on each thing Isaac and Rebekah would *not* have taken as they followed God.

COOL-IT

Right Words

Name ______________________________

Cut out the words from the bottom of the page.
Glue to the correct picture the words each child should say.

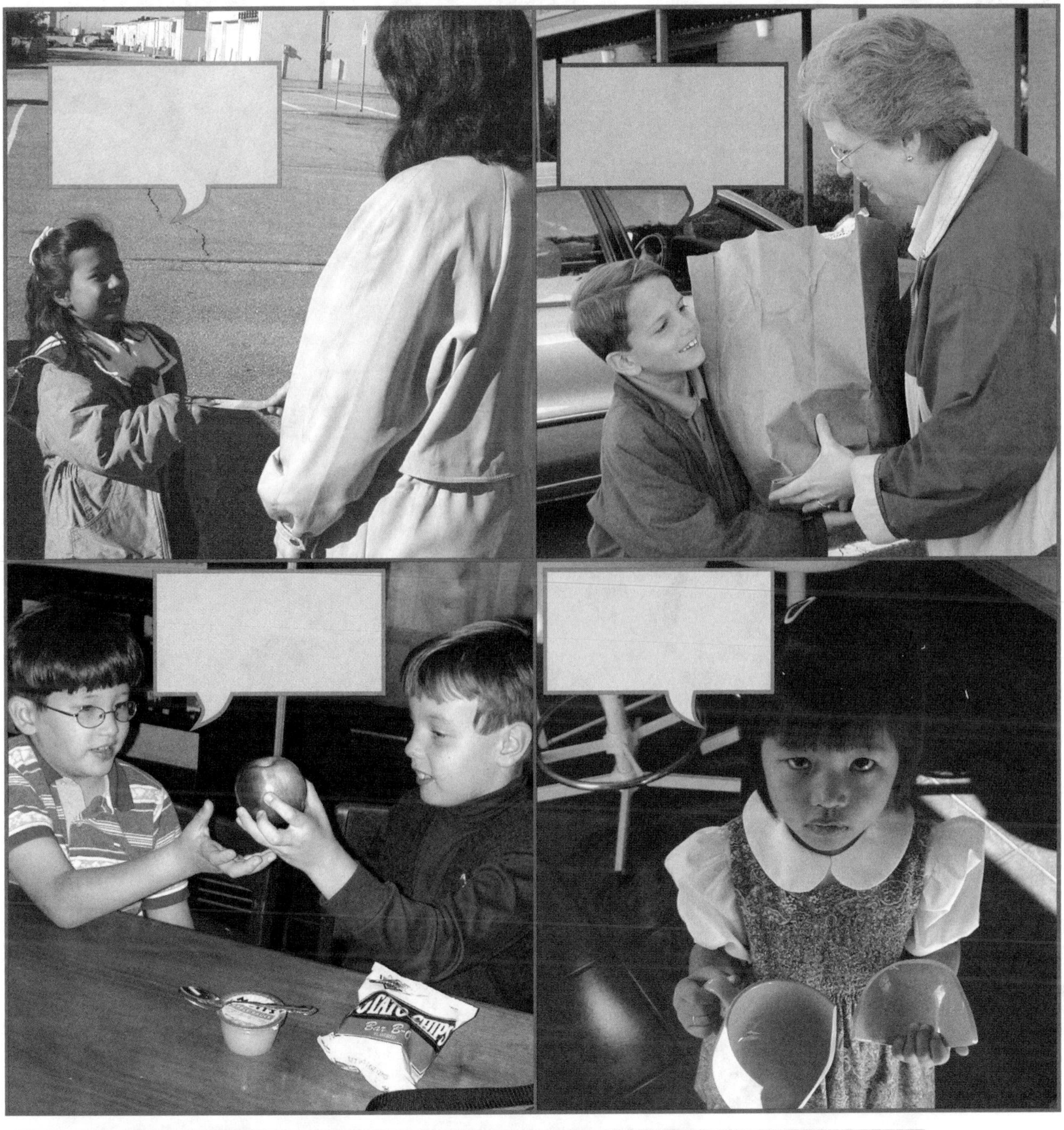

Thank you.	Jesus loves you.	I'm sorry.	May I help?

Digging Wells
Genesis 26:12-33

Name ______________________________

Circle the correct answer.

1. The enemy filled Isaac's well with dirt. yes no

2. Isaac dug the well again. yes no

3. The enemy let Isaac keep the well. yes no

4. Isaac dug another well. yes no

5. The enemy dug a well for Isaac. yes no

6. Isaac's kindness made peace with the enemy. yes no

Circle the best word to finish the sentence.

Jesus said to ______ those who hate you.

hate love

Trusting God
Isaiah 26:3

Name ______________________

God wants each person to trust Him

- for salvation.
- for needs each day.
- in times of trouble.

Finish the sentence.

I can trust God to

____

____

What does God give to those who trust Him?

Color the puzzle to find out.

1 green
2 red
3 blue
4 yellow

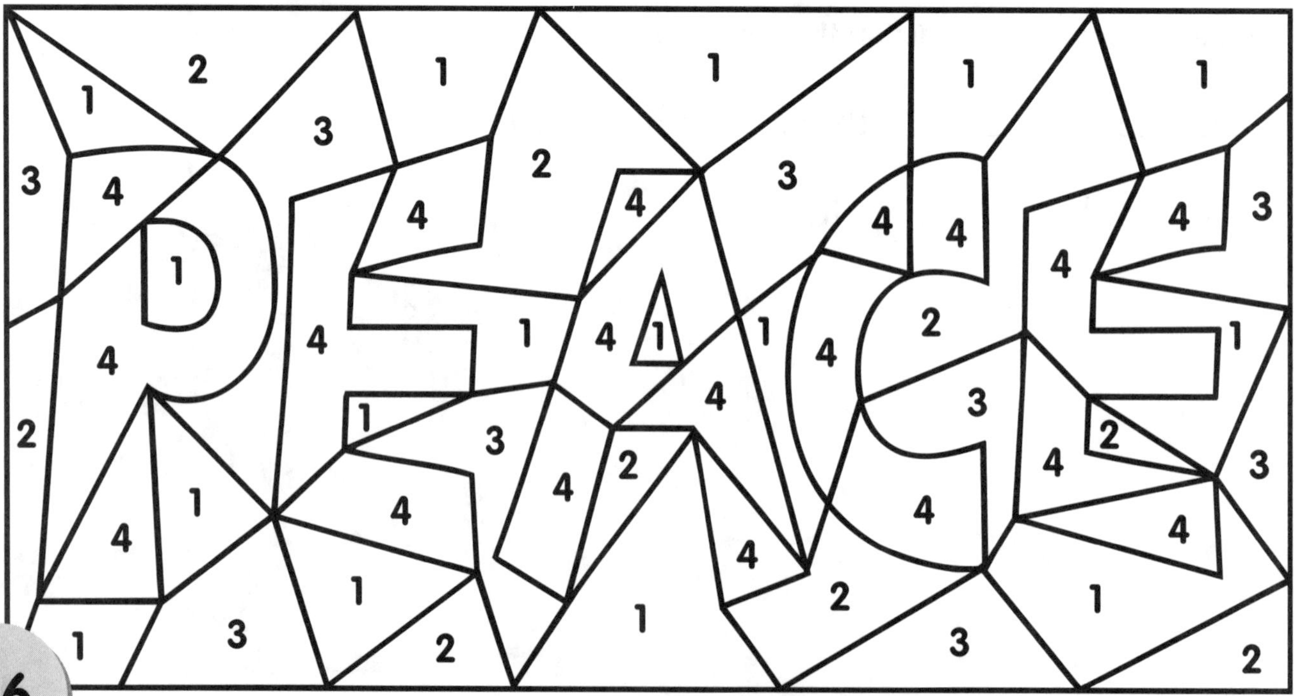

The Blessing
Genesis 26:34–27:41

Name ____________________

In the time of Jacob, the promise from a father to his oldest son was called a *blessing.* The other children served the son who had the father's blessing.

Circle the correct answer.

Jacob | Esau

1. Who was Isaac's older son?

2. Whom did God promise would receive the blessing?

3. Whom did Isaac plan to bless?

4. Whom did Isaac give the blessing to?

Answer the questions with *yes* or *no.*

5. Did Jacob lie to get his father's blessing? ____________

6. Did Jacob's lie make God happy? ____________

7. Is God happy when you lie? ____________

Ask God to help you be truthful at all times.

Reading from the Bible
References

Name ____________________

BIBLE STUDY SKILLS

The *reference* of a Bible verse has three parts.

Learn it!

Learn to read the parts of a reference.

The first part of a reference is the name of the *book*. — **John** 3:16

The next part of a reference is the *chapter*. The chapter is the first number after the name of the book. — John **3**:16

The last part of a reference is the number of the *verse*. — John 3:**16**

Practice it!

Use this reference to answer the questions.
Fill in the circle next to each correct answer.

Genesis 6:8

1. What is the name of the book in this reference?

   ○ Exodus ○ Genesis

2. What is the number of the chapter in this reference?

   ○ 6 ○ 8

3. What is the number of the verse in this reference?

   ○ 6 ○ 8

Jacob's Dream
Genesis 27:41–28:22

Name ______________________________

Esau was mad at Jacob. Jacob knew that Esau wanted to kill him. Jacob left home.

God spoke to Jacob in a dream. Jacob worshiped God.

Number the pictures in story order.

Make an *X* on the sentence God did *not* tell Jacob.

I am the Lord.
I will let Esau kill you.
I will give you this land.
I will not leave you.

Jacob Marries
Genesis 29:1-30

Name ______________________

Make an *X* under the name of the person described.

	Jacob	Laban
1. I lied to my father to get his blessing.		
2. I worked for seven years to marry my wife.		
3. I was not honest when I gave Leah in marriage instead of Rachel.		
4. I promised to work for seven more years to marry Rachel.		

Honesty pleases God.

Circle the pictures of things that please God.

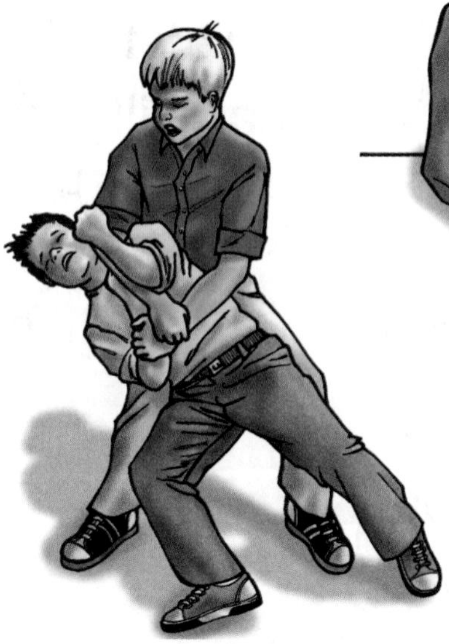

Forgiveness
Genesis 32-33

Name ____________________

Answer the questions with *yes* or *no.*

Jacob was going back home.

1. Was Jacob happy to see Esau? ______________

2. Was Jacob afraid? ______________

Jacob prayed for God's help.

Esau forgave Jacob.

3. Did Esau still want to kill Jacob? ______________

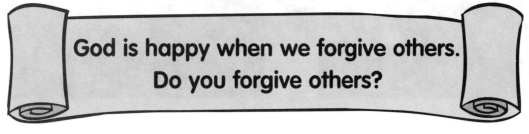

**God is happy when we forgive others.
Do you forgive others?**

A Changed Heart
Psalm 51:10

Name ______________________________

Circle the correct person.

Jacob
Esau
showed his brother that his heart had changed to good.

Make an *X* on each picture that shows a good heart.

Sold as a Slave

Genesis 37

Name ______________________________

Joseph's brothers hated him.
Joseph's brothers wanted to hurt him.

God protected Joseph.

The sin of Joseph's brothers hurt others.
My sin sometimes hurts others.

Draw a line to match the ending of each sentence.

1. Joseph was sold as a	sad.
2. Joseph's father felt	guilty.
3. Joseph's brothers felt	slave.

Color Joseph's coat to make it a coat of many colors.

Run from Sin
Genesis 39

Name ______________________

Joseph worked for an important man.
God blessed Joseph with a good master.

Joseph was tempted to sin.
Joseph ran from the sin.

God protected Joseph.

Circle the actions that please God.

What should I do when I am tempted to sin?

talk to an adult

blame someone

pray for God's help

hope I don't get caught

go away from the temptation

John 3:16
For God so loved the world...

remember a Bible verse

God Uses Others
Genesis 40-41

Name ___________________________

Joseph was in jail.
Joseph did not blame God.

Joseph helped others while in jail.
God let Joseph out of jail to help Pharaoh.

Pharaoh made Joseph a ruler.
God blessed Joseph.

Follow the path that would please God.

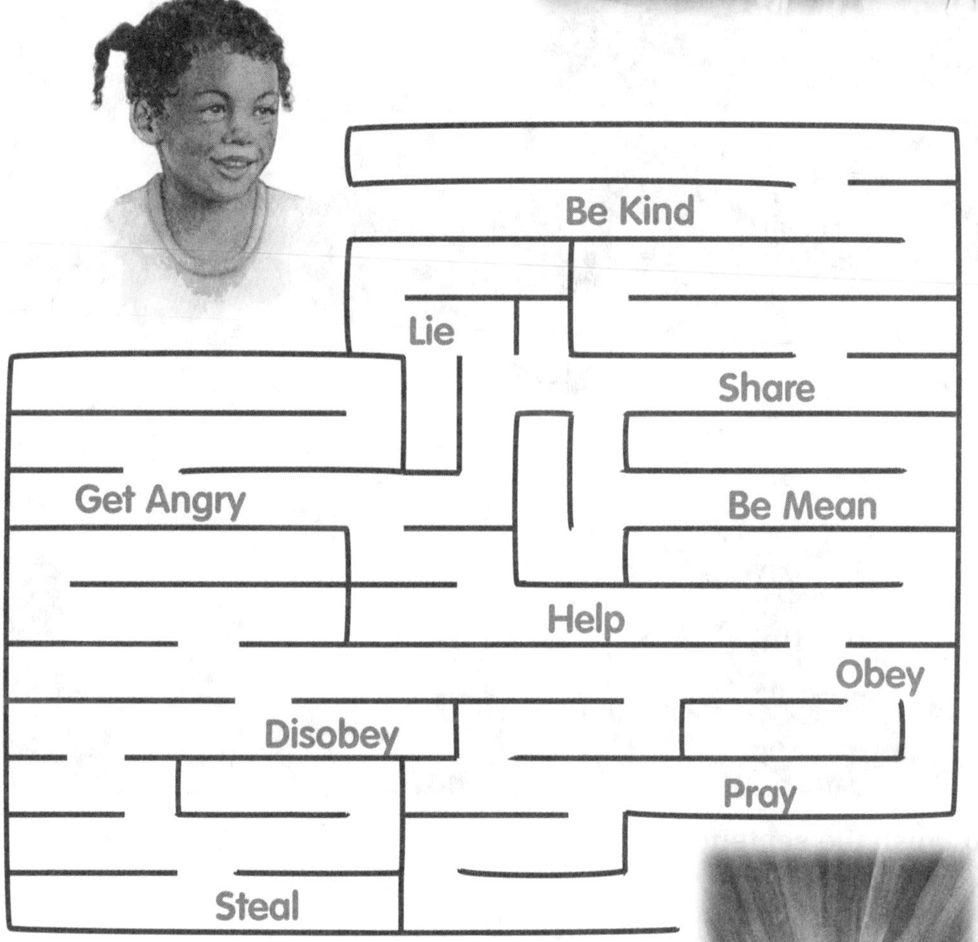
Be Kind
Lie
Share
Get Angry
Be Mean
Help
Obey
Disobey
Pray
Steal

Joseph's Secret

Genesis 42

Name ___________________________

God used Joseph to grow and store food.

There was no rain for a long time.
Joseph's family could not grow food.

Joseph gave food to his brothers.
They did not know the ruler was Joseph.

Number the pictures in story order.

Write *me* to finish the sentence.

God used Joseph to help others.

God can use ____________ to help others.

Famine and Food

Name ____________________

Use the words in the word bank to finish the sentences.

Word bank
food
rain
sun

Most food comes from plants.

1. God gives the ________________ to help plants grow.

2. God gives the ________________ to help plants grow.

3. If there is no rain, there is no ________________.

Thank God for your food each day.

Draw your favorite food for the children to share.

In God's Plan
Genesis 43-45

Name ______________________________

Joseph trusted God.
God led Joseph to be a ruler.

Make an *X* in the box next to the correct sentence for each picture.

☐ Joseph forgave his brothers.

☐ Joseph hated his brothers.

☐ Jacob kept his sons at home.

☐ Jacob was happy to hear that Joseph was alive.

☐ Joseph went to Jacob's home.

☐ Joseph's father and brothers moved to Egypt.

Joseph's Family

Name ______________________

God gave promises to Abraham.
God gave promises to Abraham's son and his grandson.

Sarah
Rebekah
Rachel
Joseph

A family tree shows the people in a family. Lines connect each son to his parents.

Cut out the pictures of Abraham, Isaac, and Jacob. Glue each picture in the correct place on the family tree.

Abraham
Isaac
Jacob

Joseph's Family (continued)

The Promised One

Luke 1:26-58

Name ____________________

God promised to send a Savior.
God always keeps His promises.

Draw a line to match the first part of the sentence with the end of the sentence. Read each completed sentence.

God sent Gabriel to	of Jesus.
Mary was to be the mother	people from their sins.
Mary's son would be	the Savior.
God sent His Son to save	give news to Mary.

Color all the scrolls that tell what Mary did after Gabriel told her the amazing news.

praised God

did not believe God

obeyed God

ran away

thanked God

Reading from the Bible
Table of Contents

Name ____________________

The table of contents at the front of your Bible groups the books into the Old Testament and the New Testament.

Use the table of contents for the New Testament to answer the questions.

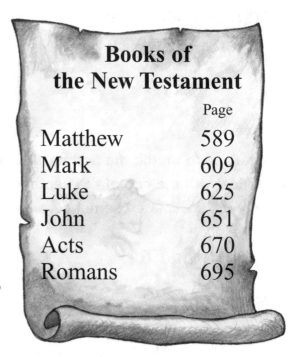

Books of the New Testament

	Page
Matthew	589
Mark	609
Luke	625
John	651
Acts	670
Romans	695

1. What is the first book of the New Testament?

   ○ Matthew ○ Mark

2. On what page does Mark begin?

   ____

3. Is Genesis in the New Testament?

   ○ yes ○ no

Use the table of contents in your Bible to answer the questions.

4. Is the New Testament before or after the Old Testament?

   ○ before ○ after

5. On what page does Matthew begin in your Bible? ________

6. On what page does Luke begin in your Bible? ________

God tells of the birth of Jesus in Luke.
Find Luke in your Bible for someone to read.

The Right Thing
Matthew 1:18-25

Name ______________________

Joseph loved God.
Joseph loved Mary.
He wanted to do the right thing.

Use a word from the word bank to finish each sentence.

1. ______________ wanted to make the right decision.

2. An angel told Joseph about Mary's son in a ______________.

3. *Emmanuel* means that ______________ is with us.

4. Joseph obeyed God and took Mary as his ______________.

dream
God
wife
Joseph

The angel spoke to Joseph in a dream.
How does God speak to us today?

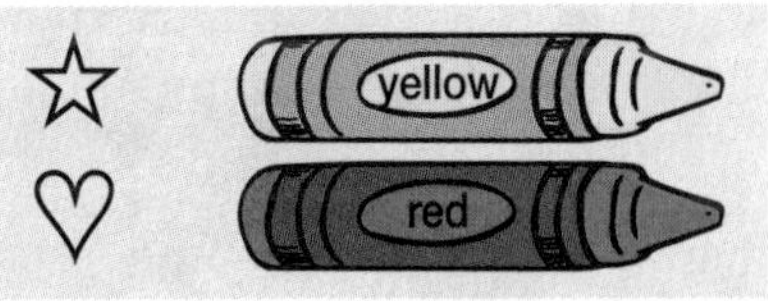

☆
♡
yellow
red

Color the shapes using the code to find out.

The Gift of Love

Name ______________________________

God gave us the gift of His Son, Jesus. Jesus was God's gift of love to all people.

Many people give gifts to each other at Christmas to show their love. How can you show your love for your parents?

Use the Christmas code to find out.

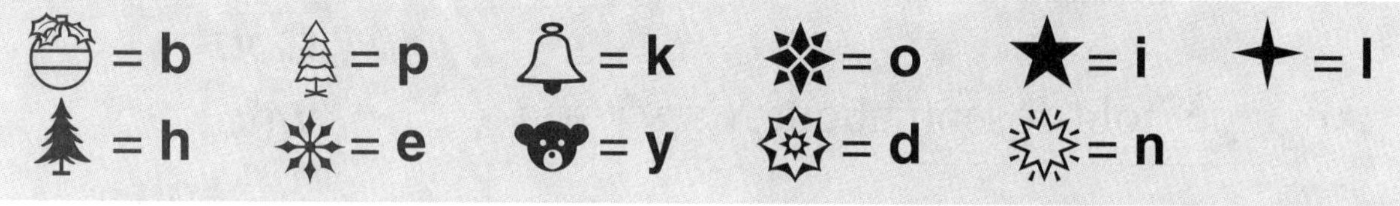

= b
= p
= k
= o
= i
= l
= h
= e
= y
= d
= n

I can
____ ____ ____ ____.

I can be
____ ____ ____ ____.

I can
____ ____ ____ ____.

Not Impossible!
Memory Reminder

Name ________________________________

1. **Color the stars.**
2. **Cut out the cover on the bold outside lines.**
3. **Fold the cover in half. Cut out the small center rectangle. Unfold and smooth flat.**
4. **Turn the cover face down and tape the top flap to the side flaps to form a pocket.**

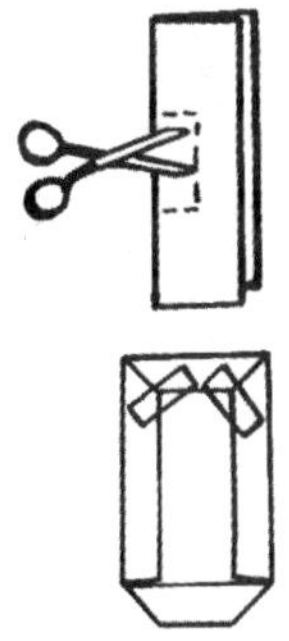

God can
do the
Impossible!
Luke 1:37

Not Impossible! (continued)

Name ____________________

1. At home, ask an adult to remove a plastic switchplate cover from the wall.
2. Slide the plastic switchplate into the cover and tape the bottom flap to the side flaps.
3. Ask an adult to reattach the switchplate to the wall.

Every time you see it, remember that *nothing is impossible* with God!

A Savior Is Born
Luke 2:1-20

Name ______________________________

The perfect time had come. God kept His promise to send a Savior.

Color the star next to the correct answer.

1. Joseph and Mary went to pay taxes in ____.
   ☆ Bethlehem
   ☆ Canaan

2. There was no room for them in the ____.
   ☆ city
   ☆ inn

3. Jesus was born in a ____.
   ☆ stable
   ☆ palace

4. Angels announced the birth of Jesus to the ____.
   ☆ Wise Men
   ☆ shepherds

Connect the dots to show Bethlehem, the town where Jesus was born.

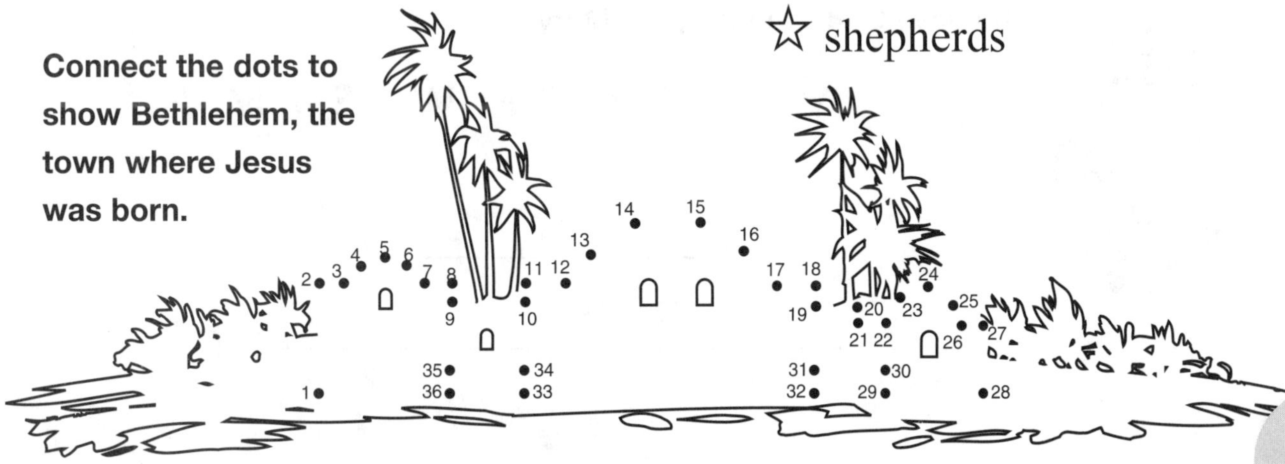
1 2 3 4 5 6 7 8 9 10 11 12 13 14 15 16 17 18 19 20 21 22 23 24 25 26 27 28 29 30 31 32 33 34 35 36

God's Messengers

Matthew 1:19-21;
Luke 1:26-33; 2:9-11

Name ______________________________

God let angels be a part of His plan. The angels delivered His messages to people on earth.

Draw a line to the people who received each angelic message.

Fear not! You are blessed and will have a son who will be the Savior!

Fear not! Don't be afraid to take Mary as your wife! Her son's name is to be Jesus.

Fear not! A Savior is born in the city of David who is Christ the Lord!

Joseph

the shepherds

Mary

Cross out letters *M, T,* and *W*. Write the remaining letters to find the name of the angel who gave God's message to Mary.

Letters to cross out:
M T W

G M W A T M B W R M W I E T M W L

_ _ _ _ _ _ _ _ _ _ _ _ _ _

Joy in the Temple
Luke 2:21-39

Name ______________________

Write the name of the correct person under each description.

I waited many years to see God's salvation! My husband died a long time ago. I lived in the temple and spent time fasting and praying.

Who am I? ______________

God promised me I would not die until I had seen the one that would save people from sin. God kept His promise. When I walked into the temple, I saw Jesus. Who am I? ______________

Mary
Joseph
Simeon
Anna

We obeyed God's laws and brought Jesus to the temple. We were amazed by what Simeon and Anna told us. Who are we?

______________ and ______________

Wise Men Worship

Matthew 2:1-23

Name ____________________

The Wise Men looked for Jesus.
They knew He was the promised King.
When they found Him, they worshiped Him.

Use the words in the word bank to solve the puzzle.

dream	gold	Herod	star	wise

Across

❋ The men who came were very ____.

🔔 The Wise Men found Mary, Joseph, and Jesus in a ____.

★ The men followed a ____.

🌲 One of the gifts the Wise Men brought was ____.

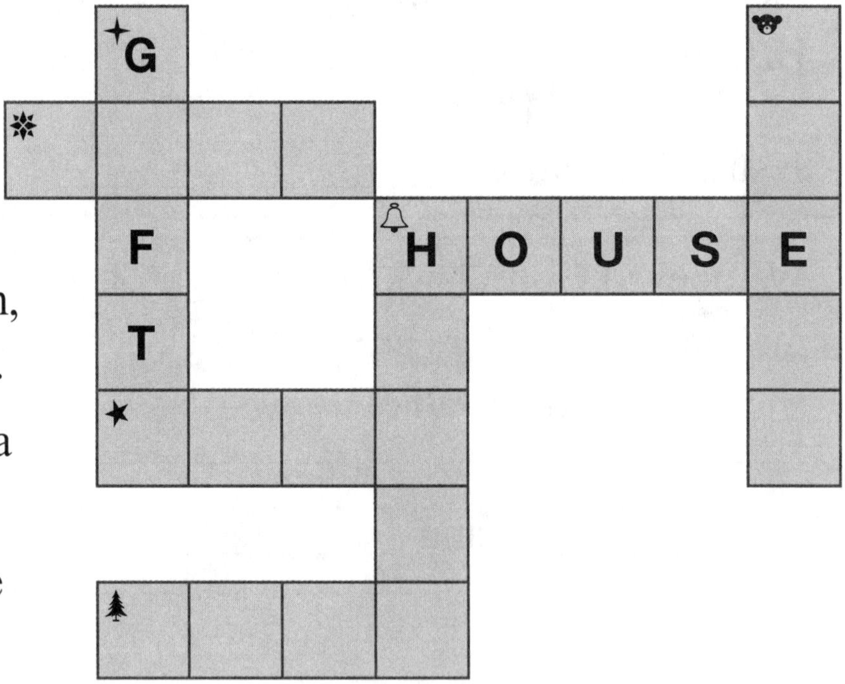

G
F
T
H O U S E

Down

✦ The Wise Men brought three ____.

🐻 God spoke to the Wise Men in a ____.

🔔 The evil King ____ wanted to kill Jesus.

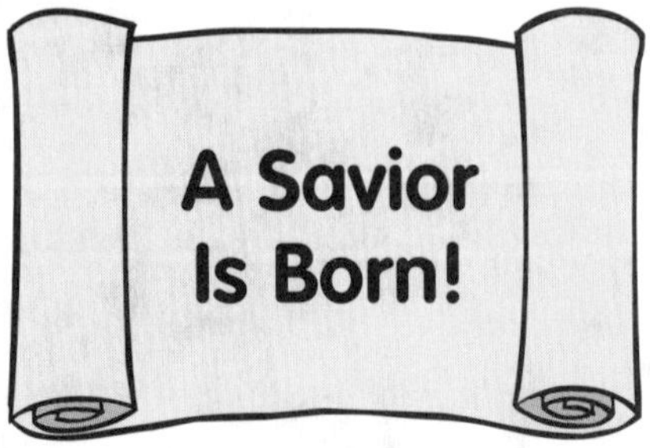

A Savior Is Born!

The Light of Christ

Name ____________________

The Wise Men followed the star.
The star led them to Jesus.
The Wise Men worshiped Jesus.
Do you worship Jesus?

1. **Color the suncatcher with bright colors using crayons or colored pencils. Press down firmly while coloring.**
2. **Put about a tablespoon of vegetable oil on a cotton ball. Dab the oil over the suncatcher. Use a tissue to blot off excess oil. Be careful not to smear the colors.**
3. **Cut out the suncatcher.**
4. **Punch two holes at the top. Insert string in the holes to form a hanger.**
5. **Hang the suncatcher in the window and remember that Christ is the Light of the world!**

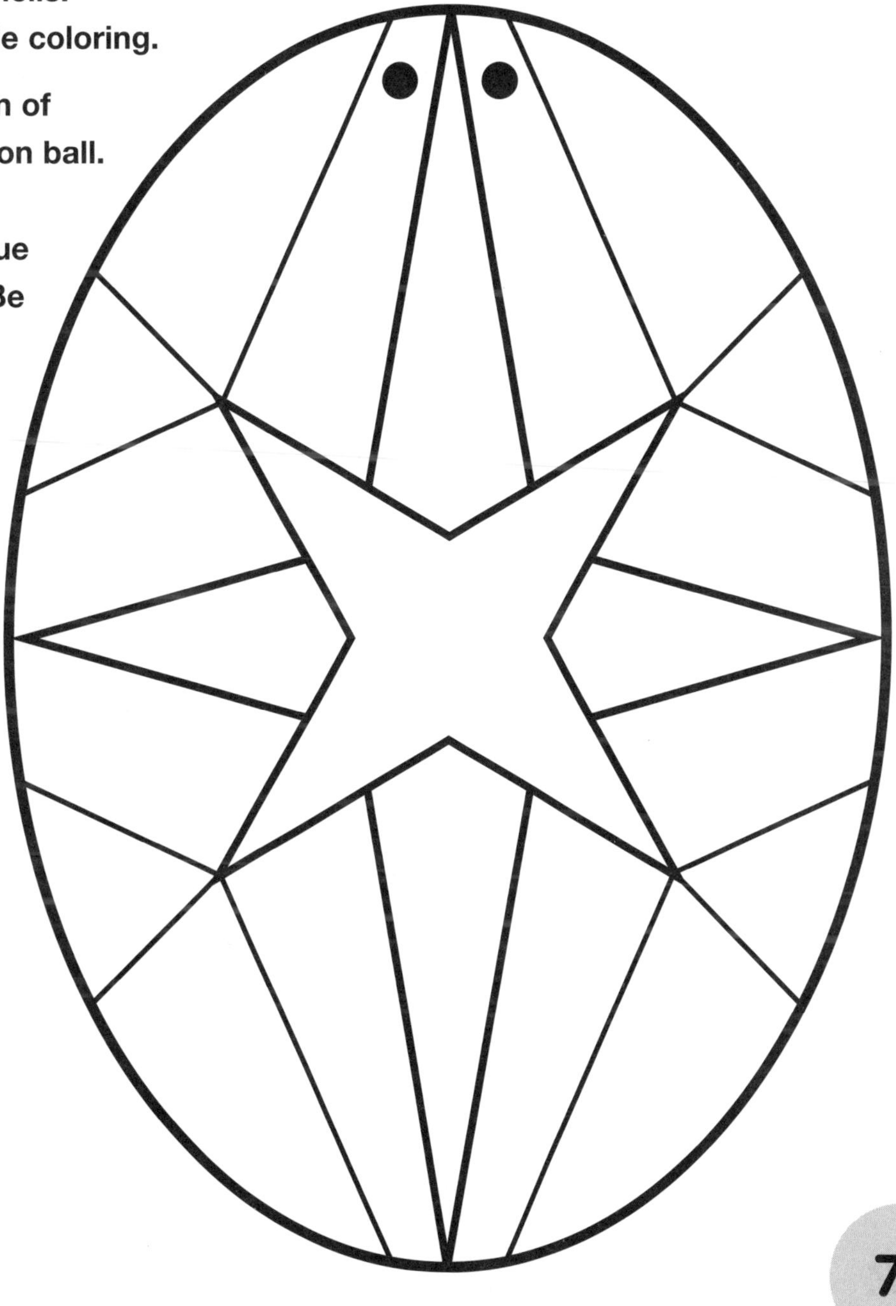

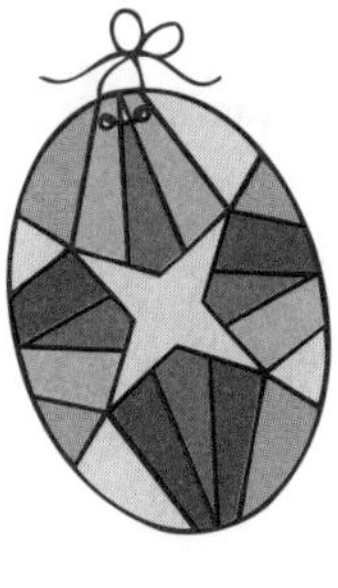

The Light of Christ (continued)

A Leader Is Born

Exodus 1:8–2:10

Name ____________________

Pharaoh was afraid of God's people.
He made a law to kill the baby boys.
God took care of baby Moses.
Whom did God use to care for Moses?

Draw a line to match each sentence to the correct picture.

1. I made a basket to hide my baby.

2. I found the baby's basket in the river.

3. I ran to get the baby's mother to take care of him.

Miriam

Moses' mother

Pharaoh's daughter

Connect the dots to finish the picture. Start at the star and count by 5s. Color the picture.

★
5
10
15
20
25
30
35
40
45
50
55
60
65
70
75
80
85
90
95
100

A Light for Jesus
Matthew 5:16

Name ______________________________

God wants Christians to be lights in a sinful world.

Color the candle next to each picture that shows God's light shining.

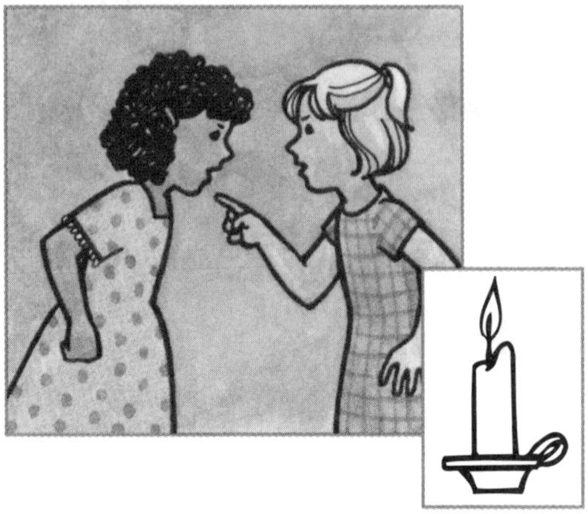

Songs

HOLY BIBLE

God Says "Obey!"

Exodus 2:11–4:20

Name ______________________

God gave Moses a job.
Moses made excuses.
God wanted Moses to obey.

Aaron
hand obey
Moses
snake

Use the words in the word bank to finish the sentences.

1. God promised to help ______________
2. God turned Moses' rod into a ______________.
3. God covered Moses' ______________ with leprosy.
4. God sent ______________ to help Moses.
5. Moses said he would ______________ God.

Color the puzzle to find when God wants us to obey.

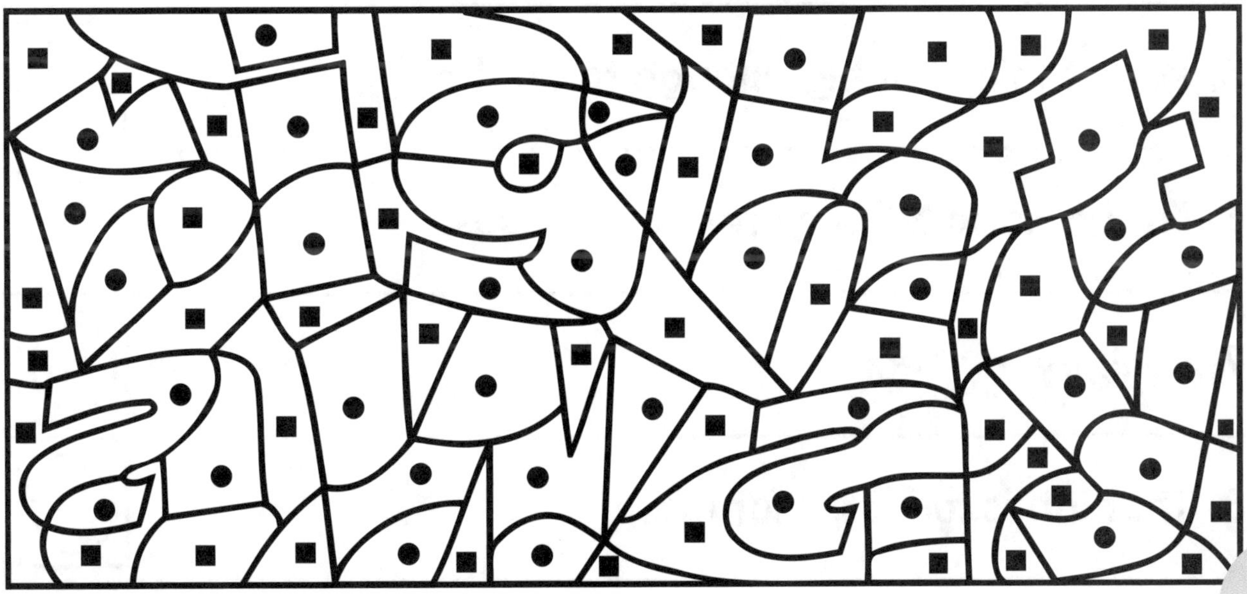

Excuses

Name ___________________________

God has jobs for you to do.
Do you make excuses like Moses did?
What does God think of the answers you give?

Finish each face to show what God thinks about the answer. Draw a smile if the answer pleases God. Draw a frown if the answer makes God sad.

1. I am too busy.	
2. Yes. I'll do it right now.	
3. Someone else should do it.	
4. I know God will help me finish this job.	
5. I don't think I'm big enough to do that.	
6. I'm afraid to tell anyone about Jesus.	
7. I will try my best.	
8. That job is too hard for me.	

God's Power
Exodus 7-10

Name ______________________________

Pharaoh would not obey God. God must punish sin. God sent plagues to show His power.

Use the words in the word bank to finish the puzzle.

hail
darkness
locusts
blood
frogs

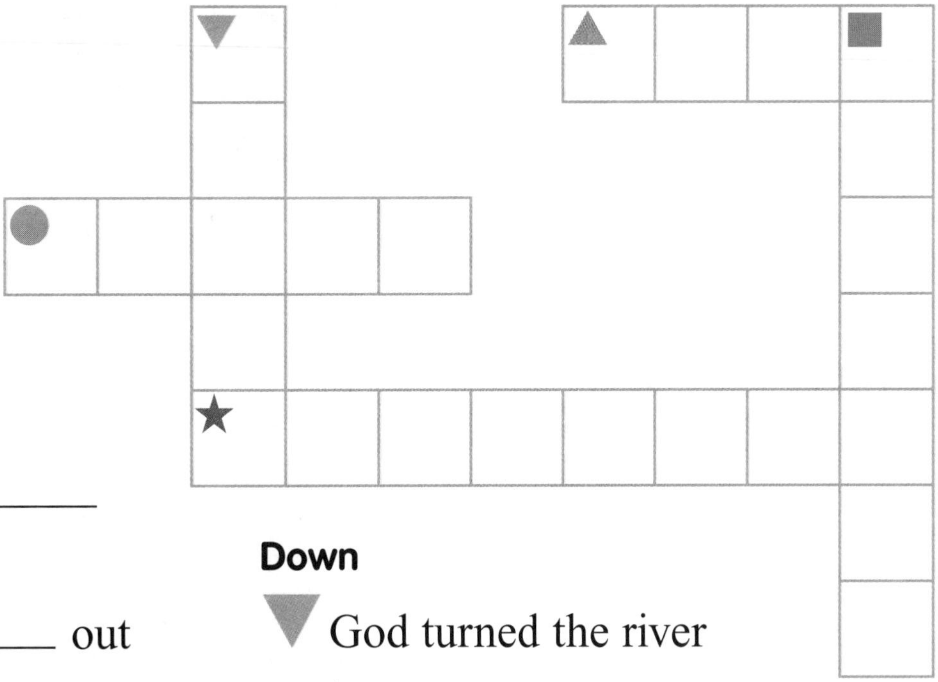

Across

▲ God rained _____ on Egypt.

● God sent _____ out of the river.

★ God covered Egypt with _____.

Down

▼ God turned the river to _____.

■ God sent _____ to eat the green plants.

The Passover
Exodus 11:1–12:36

Name ______________________

Write the letter of the correct sentence ending on each blank.

1. The Israelites packed to ______
2. Some Egyptians gave them ______
3. Each family ate a special ______
4. This meal is called the Passover because death ______

A. gold and silver jewelry.

B. passed over the Israelites.

C. leave Egypt.

D. meal together.

Each family killed a perfect lamb. They spread its blood to save them from death.

God sent His perfect Son to die to save people from eternal death.

Help the Israelite father paint the door as God commanded in Exodus 12:7.

A Path Through the Sea
Exodus 14:10-31

Name ______________________

Moses and the Israelites trusted God. God made a way for His people to walk through the Red Sea.

Follow the directions on page 80 to watch the water of the sea turn to dry ground.

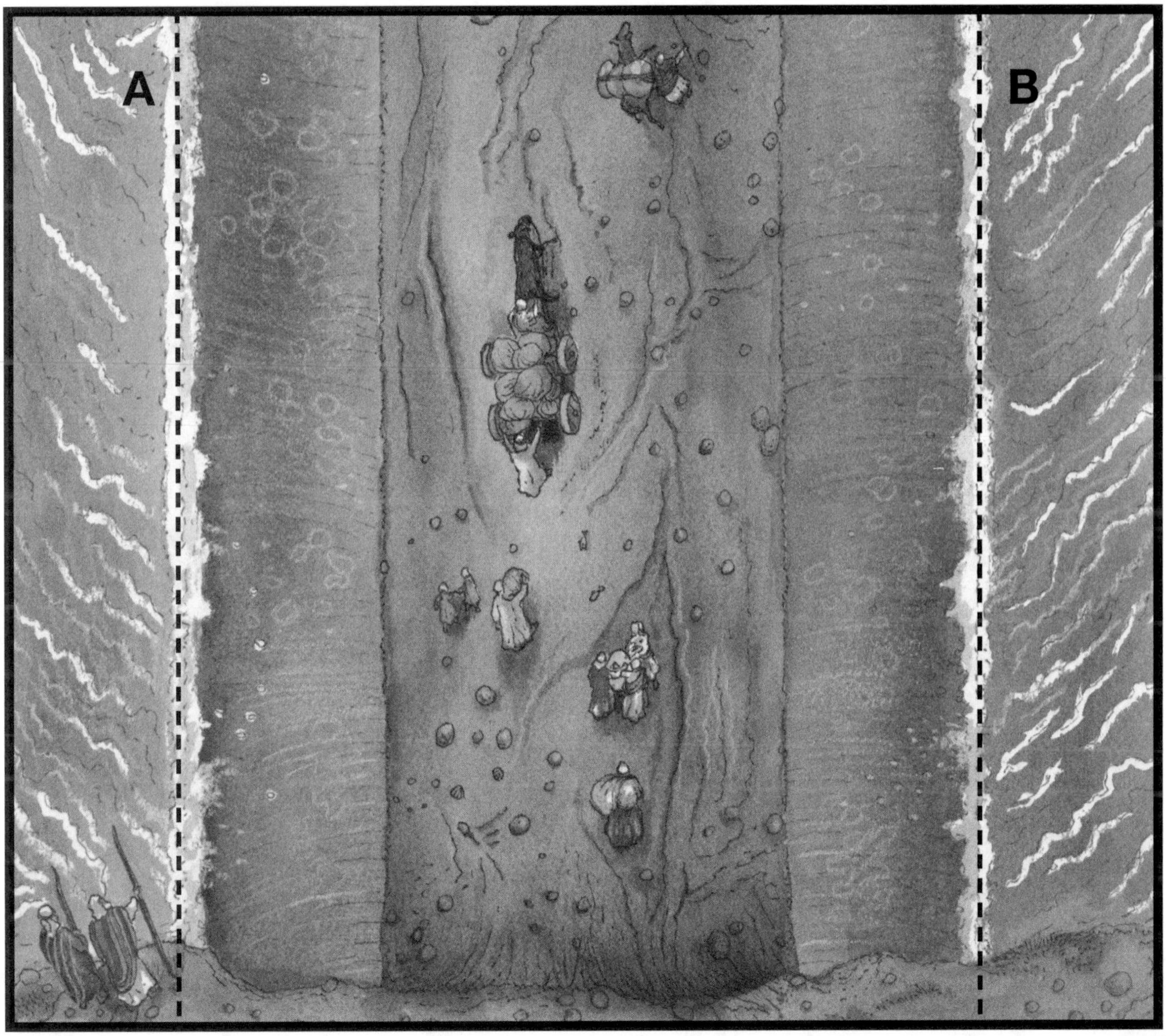
A
B

A Path Through the Sea (continued)

1. Cut on the heavy outside line.
2. Fold left edge back along dotted line A.
3. Fold right edge back along dotted line B.
4. Turn page over.
5. Fold A back on dotted line C.
6. Fold B back on dotted line D.
7. Turn over and keep folded so A and B touch.
8. Use the visual to tell the story of God's power and protection. Pull A and B apart to watch the Red Sea part and the people cross on dry ground.

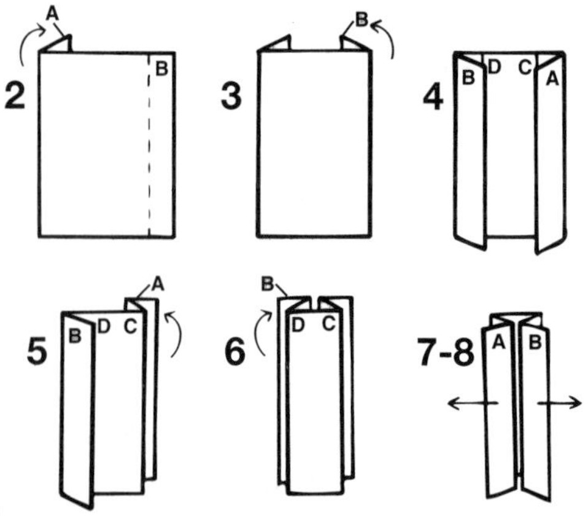
2
3
4
5
6
7-8
A
B
C
D

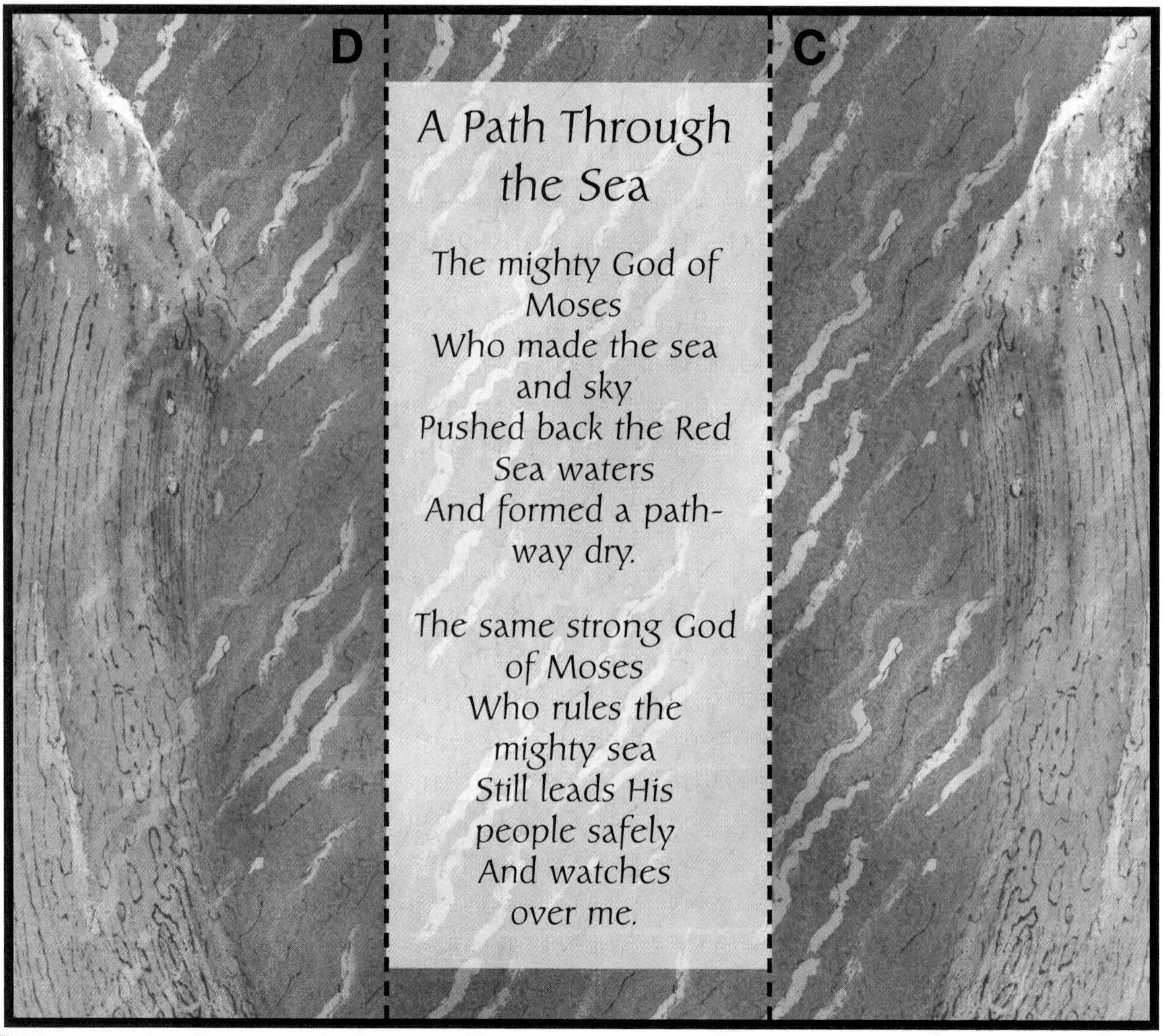
D
C
A Path Through the Sea
The mighty God of Moses
Who made the sea and sky
Pushed back the Red Sea waters
And formed a path-way dry.
The same strong God of Moses
Who rules the mighty sea
Still leads His people safely
And watches over me.

God Leads His People

Exodus 13:20-22

Name ______________________________

Use the words in the word bank to finish the sentences.

fire	cloud

1. God led the Israelites with a pillar of ______________ in the day.

2. God led the Israelites with a pillar of ______________ at night.

Follow the lines and write the correct letters in the boxes.
Read the letters down in their new order to answer the question.

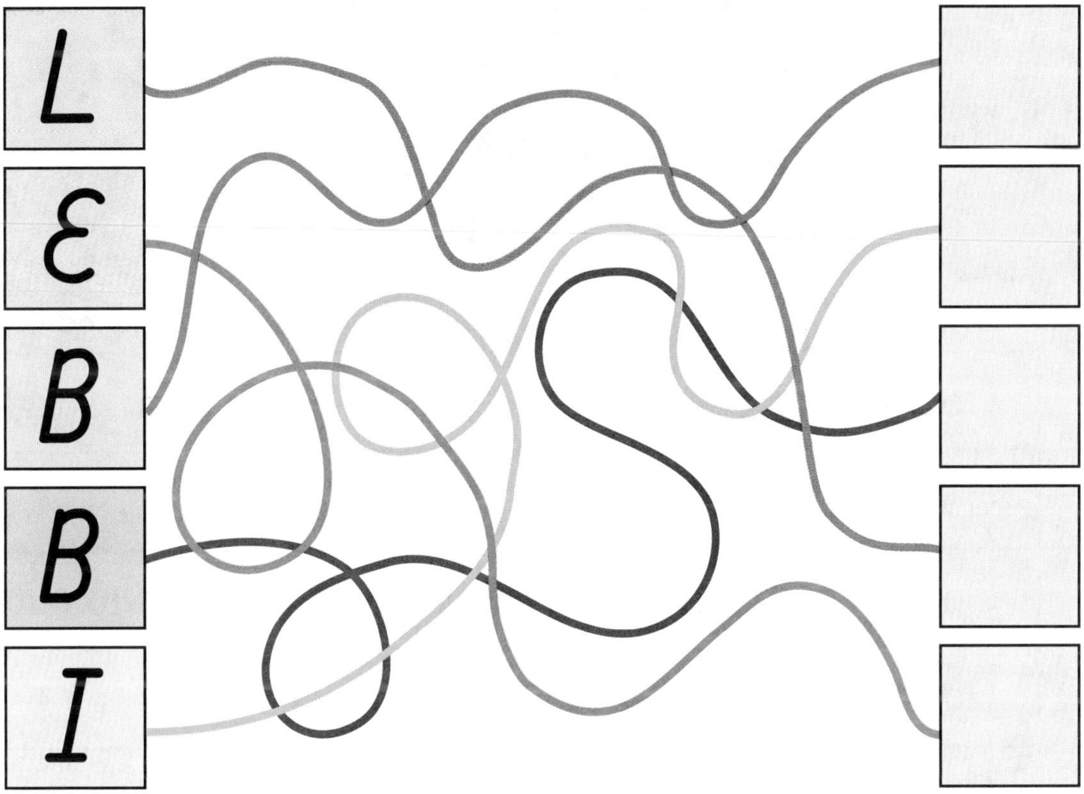
L
E
B
B
I

3. How does God lead Christians today? the ______________

God Helps

Name ______________________________

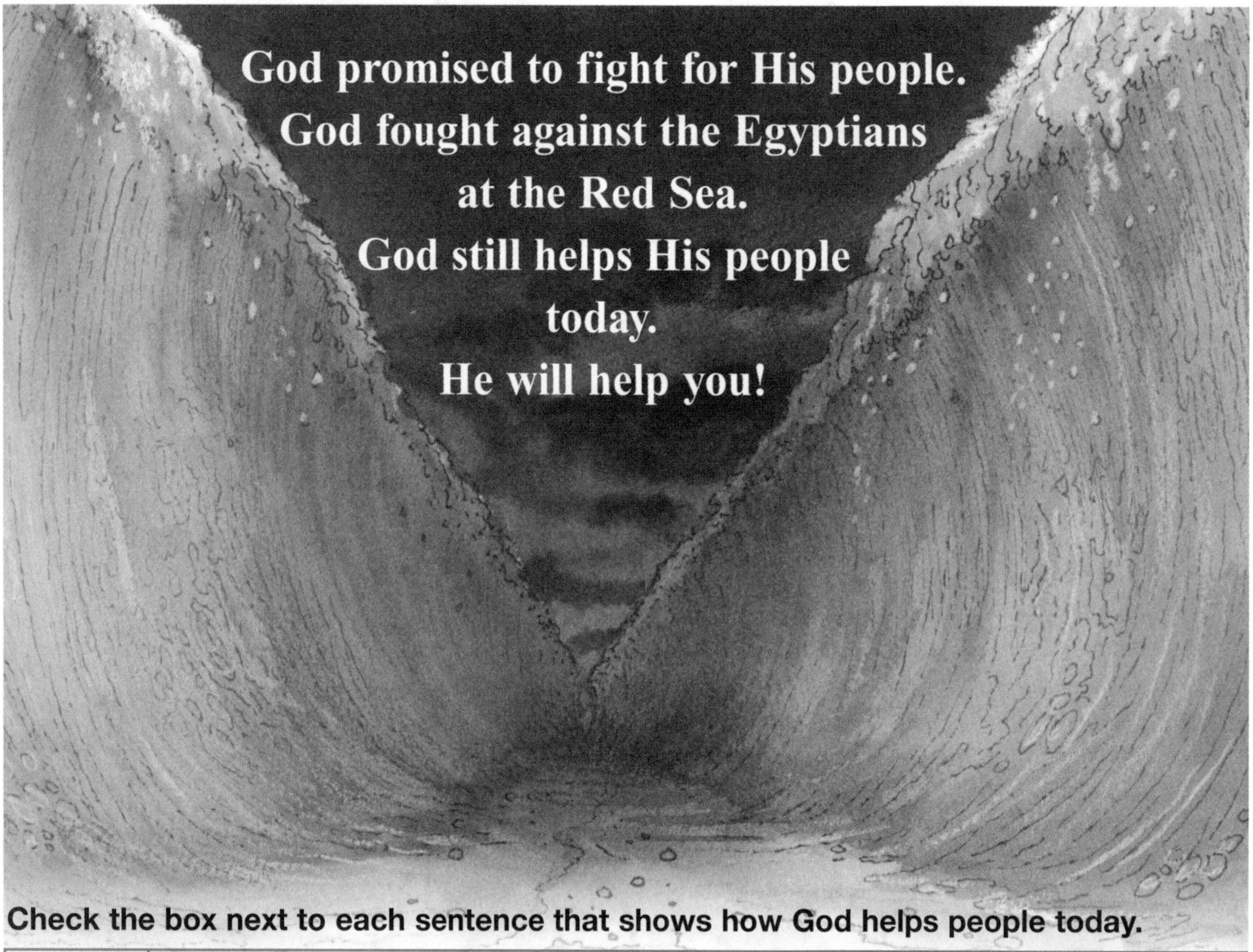

God promised to fight for His people.
God fought against the Egyptians at the Red Sea.
God still helps His people today.
He will help you!

Check the box next to each sentence that shows how God helps people today.

	God gives people the Bible to teach them what is right.
	God wants people to trust themselves.
	God gives children their parents to teach them to obey.
	God gives preachers who warn about sin.
	God gives rules to help us live safely.
	God gives everyone a lot of money.
	God listens to Christians when they pray.

Complaining Is Sin!
Exodus 15:22–16:21

Name ____________________

God's people complained. They did not trust Him. But even when His people disobeyed, God cared for them.

Acacia tree in desert

Fill in the circle next to the correct word to finish each sentence.

1. The people complained when they found only bitter _____ at Marah.
   - ○ water
   - ○ grapes

2. God told Moses to put a _____ in the water so the people could drink.
   - ○ stone
   - ○ tree

3. The people complained when they were _____.
   - ○ hungry
   - ○ happy

4. God sent _____ from heaven for the people to eat.
   - ○ manna
   - ○ peaches

5. God sent _____ so the people would have meat.
   - ○ ducks
   - ○ quail

The Law of God

Exodus 20:1-17; 32:1-35

Name ______________________

Use the words in the word bank to answer the questions.

obey
ten
Mt. Sinai

1. Where was Moses when God gave him the commandments? ______________________

2. How many commandments did God give? ______________

3. What does God want each of us to do with His law? ______________

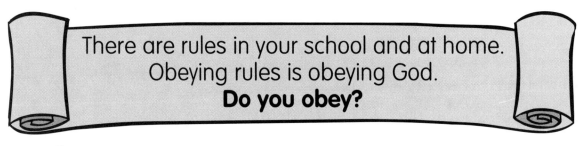

There are rules in your school and at home.
Obeying rules is obeying God.
Do you obey?

Color the [tablets] **beside each good rule.**

4. Listen when adults speak.
5. Make loud noises when others are reading.
6. Keep your desk neat.
7. Be helpful to others.
8. Take things that are not yours.

Reading from the Bible
References

Name ______________________

BIBLE STUDY SKILLS

Remember that a reference has three parts.

Genesis 1:1

book chapter:verse

Write *yes* or *no* for each sentence.

1. For **Exodus 2:4**, the book is Exodus. ____________

A – between numbers means "through."

2. For **Exodus 4:5**, the chapter is 5. ____________

3. For **Exodus 12:24-25**, the verses are 24 through 25. ____________

Write the reference of each verse.

4. Exodus, chapter twenty, verse three

____

5. Exodus, chapter twenty, verses three through seventeen ____________________________________

Keeping God's Laws

Name ____________________

God loves obedience.
God blesses those who obey His laws.

Draw a smile on the face that shows obedience to God's laws. Draw a frown on the face that shows disobedience to God's laws.

I want a new toy too!

I can help by setting the table.

God's Word teaches truth. It tells who we are and what we need. God has provided for us!

Use the code to finish each sentence.

God's laws teach that every person is a

♡	△	◇	◇	□	☆

Every person needs the

♡	○	▭	△	▽	☆

○	= a
□	= e
△	= i
◇	= n
▽	= o
☆	= r
♡	= s
▭	= v

Twelve Spies
Numbers 13-14

Name ______________________

1. Cut out shapes A and B on the heavy lines.
2. Place A on B.
3. To attach A to B, push a brass fastener through the center dots.

Use the picture wheel to tell the story of the twelve spies.

A

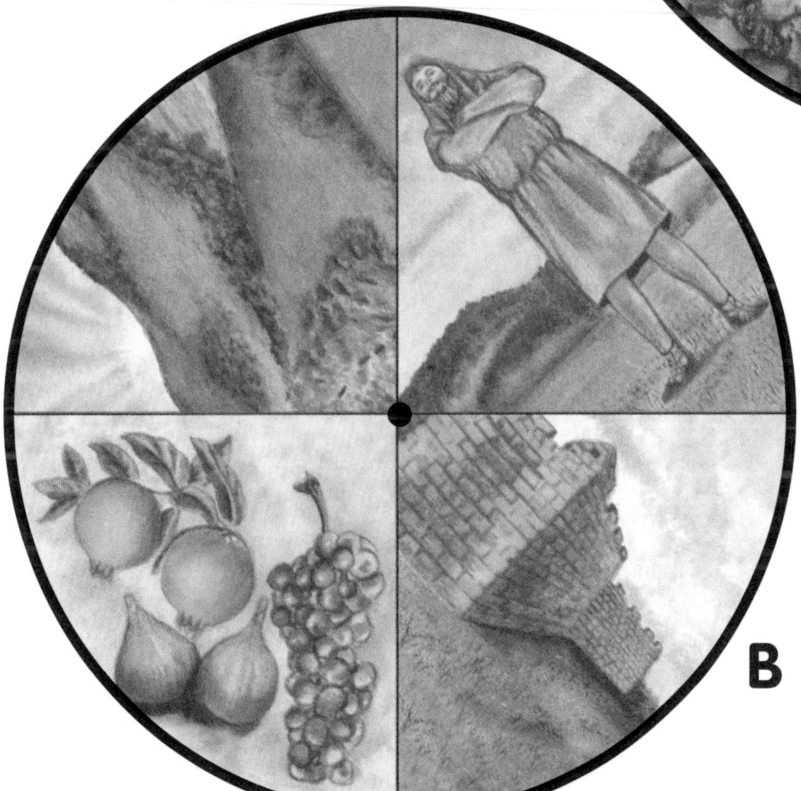

B

Twelve Spies (continued)

God sent twelve men into the beautiful land He had promised to give them.
Ten men saw giants and strong cities and were afraid.
Caleb and Joshua saw a land God would give His people.

The Red Cord

Joshua 2:1-24

Name ______________________________

Circle the correct word to finish each sentence.

1. Joshua sent two / three spies to Jericho.

2. Rahab hid the men in her barn / house.

3. God saved Rahab / Mary because she believed and protected the spies.

Connect the dots in alphabetical order to complete the picture.
Draw Rahab hanging a red cord in her window.

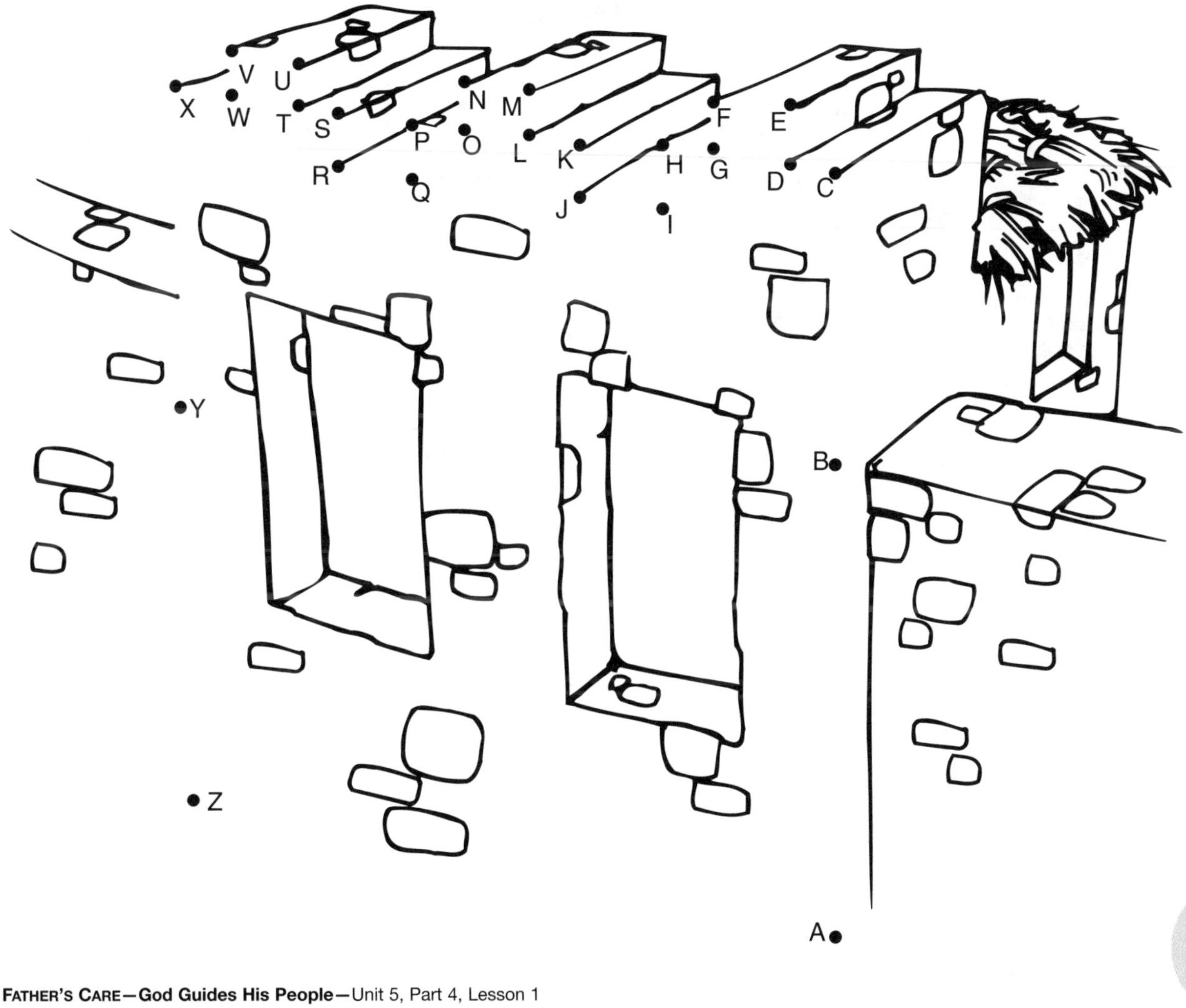

X
V
W
U
T
S
R
P
Q
N
O
M
L
K
J
H
I
F
G
E
D
C
B
A
Y
Z

Across the River

Joshua 3-4

Name ______________________________

God told His people to step into the Jordan River. As the people obeyed, God dried up the water!

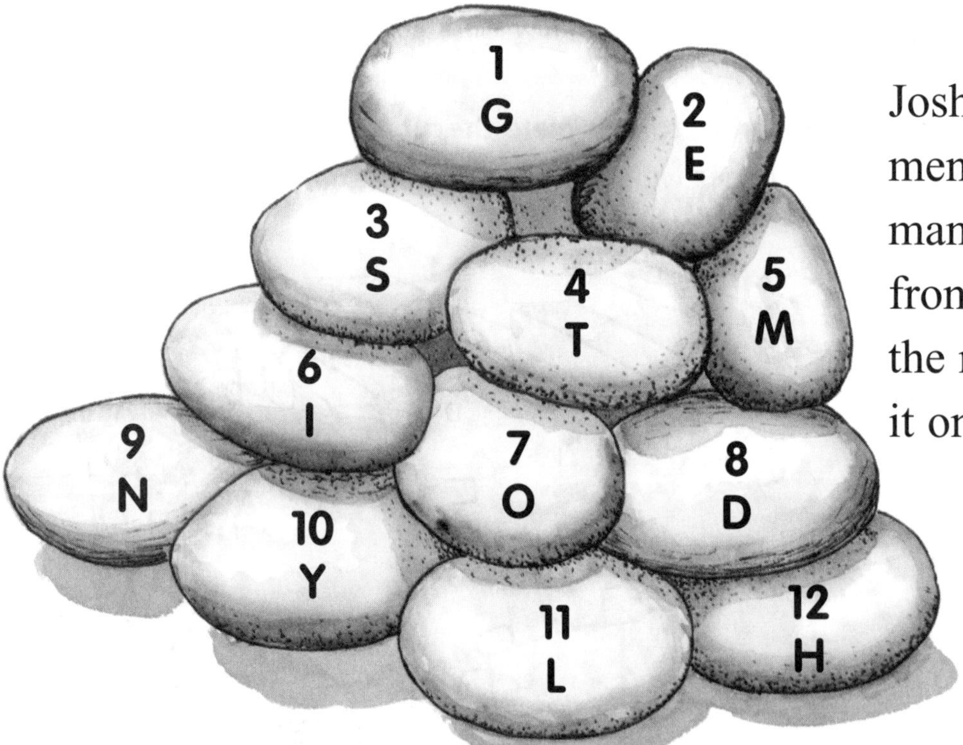

1 G
2 E
3 S
4 T
5 M
6 I
7 O
8 D
9 N
10 Y
11 L
12 H

Joshua gave twelve men a job. Each man carried a stone from the middle of the river and piled it on the shore.

Use the code on the stones to answer the question.

What did the stones help the people remember?

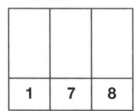

1	7	8

6	3

5	6	1	12	4	10

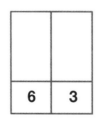

Around the City
Joshua 5:10–6:27

Name ______________________________

The people obeyed God's directions.
God gave them the victory at Jericho.

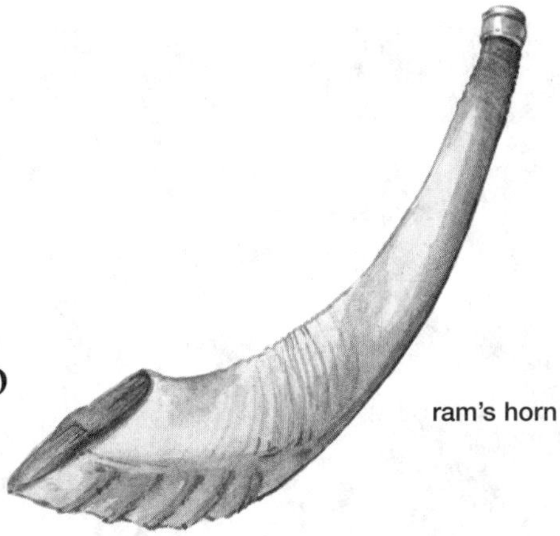
ram's horn

Write in the blank the letter of the word that finishes each sentence.

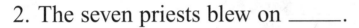

1. The people marched around Jericho one time each day for _____ days.
2. The seven priests blew on _____.
3. The seventh day, the people marched around Jericho _____ times.
4. The people gave a loud _____ and the walls fell.
5. The men looked for the red cord in Rahab's _____.

A. trumpets
B. window
C. six
D. seven
E. shout

Draw a ram's horn trumpet for the priest without a trumpet to blow.
Color the picture.

God's Love and Mercy

Psalm 103:11

Name ____________________

The Bible says that God's love and mercy is so great, it is as high as heaven! God wants everyone to love Him too.

Our love is shown by what we do.

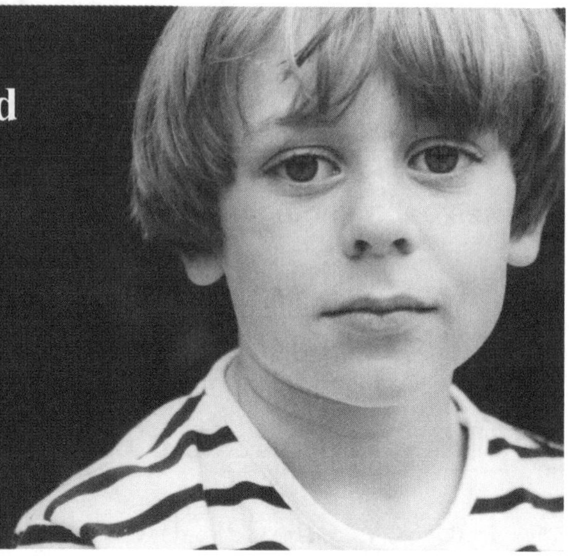

Color the heart if the action of the person shows belief in God.

♡	Abigail disobeyed her mom and lied about it. Abigail knew she had sinned. She prayed and asked God to forgive her.
♡	Hunter took a candy bar at the store. Someone saw him and told his dad. Hunter was angry that he got caught.
♡	Sharon went to Sunday school every week. Her teacher said every person needs a Savior. Sharon did not think she was bad enough to need a Savior.
♡	Derek listened to his mom as she read about heaven. He knew he could never be good enough to get to heaven by himself. He believed that Jesus was the only way to heaven.

To Be like Others
I Samuel 8

Name ______________________________

The Israelites wanted a king. Samuel told them that God was their King. They wanted a king on earth so they would be like other countries.

Answer the question.

Who is to be King of the lives ______________

of all people? ______________

God told Samuel to let the people have a king. Samuel warned them that having a king would change their lives.

Color the crown for each sentence that tells something that would happen by having a king.

1. Their sons would drive his chariots.
2. Their daughters would cook his food.
3. The people would have time to rest.
4. The best fields would be taken by the king.
5. The people would be servants to the king.

Answer the questions.

Does God want Christians to be like others? ______________

Whom does God want them to be like? ______________

God Chooses a King

I Samuel 9-10

Name ____________________

Fill in the circle of the correct answer.

1. What was Saul doing?
   - ○ He was looking for his father's lost donkeys.
   - ○ He was looking for firewood.

2. Whom did Saul and his servant talk to?
   - ○ a farmer
   - ○ Samuel

3. What did Samuel tell Saul about the donkeys?
   - ○ He should look for the donkeys in the field.
   - ○ The donkeys had been found.

4. What did Samuel tell Saul about his future?
   - ○ Saul would become king.
   - ○ Saul would become Samuel's son.

Saul and his servant went to the man of God for help. Do you go to God for help?

The King Disobeys God

I Samuel 15

Name ______________________

Use the words in the crown to finish the sentences.

Saul was a brave king.

1. Saul ______________ the battle.

God told Saul what to do when he won.

2. Saul did not ______________ God.

God had to punish Saul.

3. God would choose a new ______________.

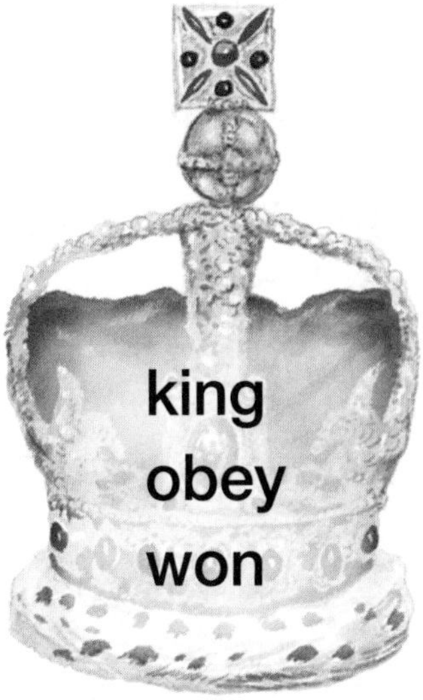
king
obey
won

Start at the ★. Count by 2s to connect the dots. See what Samuel heard when he went to Saul. Color the picture.

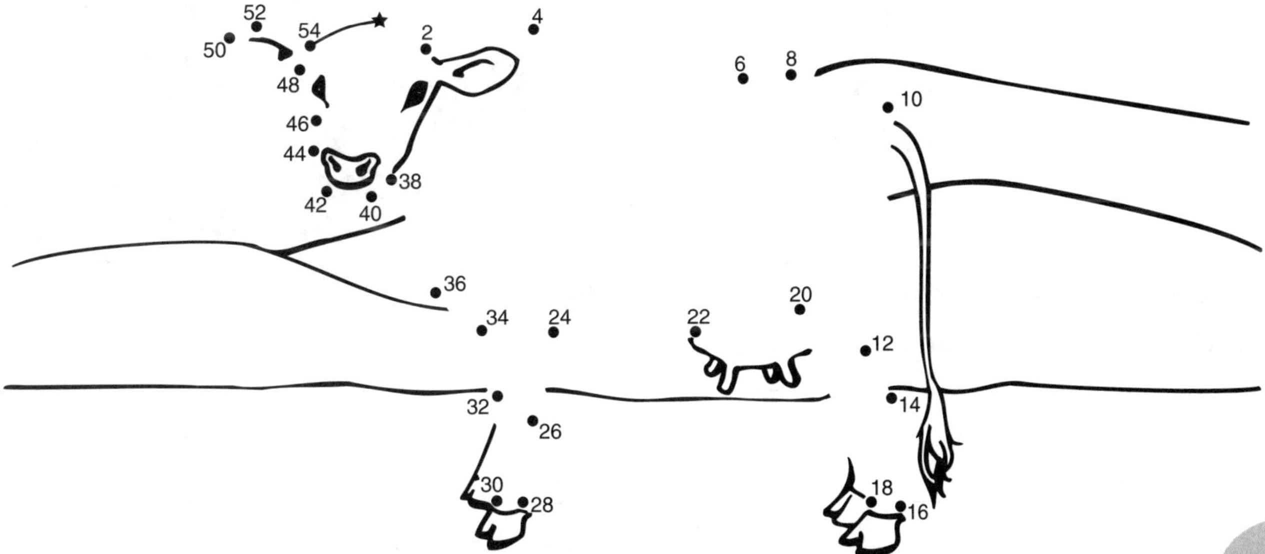

Saul's Choice
I Samuel 15

Name ______________________

God told Saul to kill the enemy.
God told Saul to kill their animals, too.

Color the sheep for each correct answer.

1. Did Saul obey God?
   - yes
   - no
2. What did Saul say he kept the animals for?
   - to worship God
   - to feed his family
3. Did Saul's choice please God?
   - yes
   - no
4. What did God want more than sacrifices?
   - He wanted Saul to keep the animals.
   - He wanted Saul to obey.

God said Saul would no longer be king. Have you ever been told you could not do something because you disobeyed?

Write a sentence about a time you could not do something because you did not obey.

____

____

Looking on the Heart

I Samuel 16:1-13

Name ______________________

God told Samuel there would be a new king. Samuel followed God to Jesse.

Samuel saw seven of Jesse's tall, handsome sons. No, the new king was not one of them.

God saw David's brave, loving heart. Yes, David was God's choice!

Use the words in the word bank to finish the puzzle.

heart	outside
inside	sheep

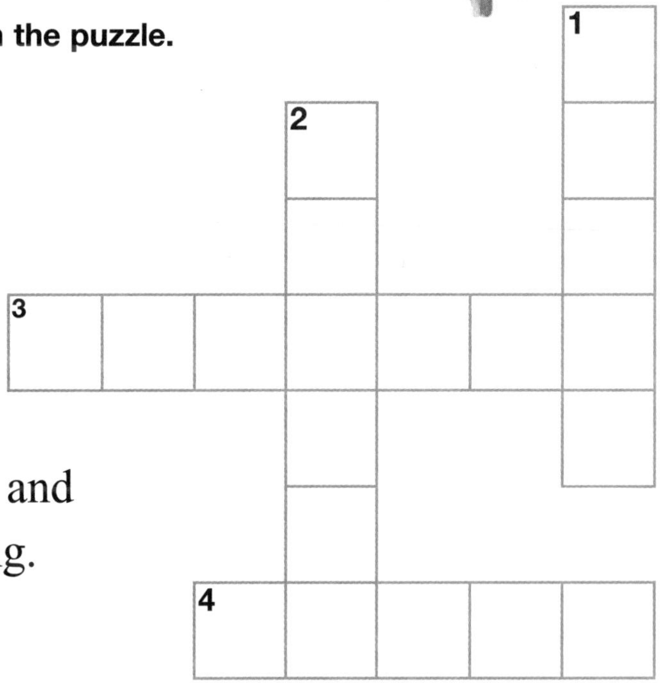

1
2
3
4

Across

3. God told Samuel that people look at others on the _____.
4. God saw the _____ of David and knew he would be a good king.

Down

1. David was keeping his father's _____.
2. The heart of a person is how he is on the _____.

What does God see when He looks on your heart?

David Serves

I Samuel 16:14-23

Name ______________________________

Use the code to fill in the missing word for each sentence.
Write the letter of the note that matches each space.

♪	♪	♪	♪	♪	♪	♪	♪
a	l	m	o	p	r	u	y

1. David played the h ___ ___ ___ while he watched sheep.

2. David played his harp for King S ___ ___ ___.

3. David's music made King Saul h ___ ___ ___ ___.

4. David carried King Saul's a ___ ___ ___ ___ for battles.

David Trusted God

I Samuel 17

Name ______________________________

Follow the directions on page 100.

1
2
Apply glue here.
Goliath shouted in pride to God's people.
Goliath wanted to fight.
David trusted God to help him kill Goliath.
3

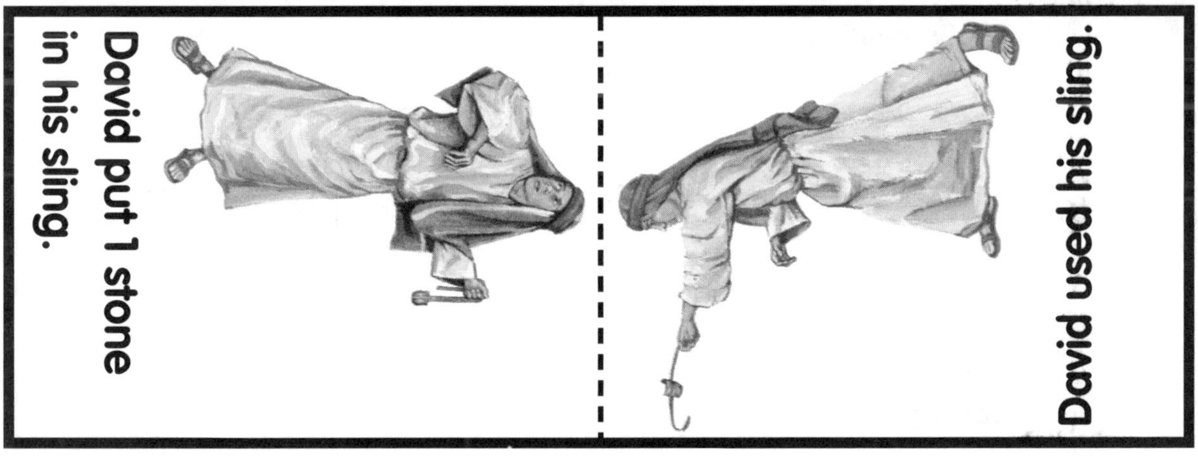
David put 1 stone in his sling.
David used his sling.

David Trusted God (continued)

Name ______________________________

<u>Preparing David:</u>

1. Cut around David on the heavy line, keeping both pictures together.
2. Turn David over; place pencil point in rectangle.
3. Tape in place.
4. Fold on dotted line between heads.
5. Open flat and apply glue to outer edges. Refold, creasing on dotted line.
6. Holding pencil between palms, quickly rub hands back and forth to see David throw his sling.

<u>Preparing Goliath:</u>

1. Cut around Goliath on the heavy line, keeping pictures together.
2. Fold on the three dotted lines.
3. Glue panel 3 to the glue flap.
4. Stand Goliath to face David and turn each panel as the story is retold. Remember to have Goliath fall for the last picture!

Apply glue here.

Fold here.

Tape pencil here.

Apply glue here.

Reading from the Bible
Finding a Verse

Name ______________________________

BIBLE STUDY SKILLS

Learn it! **Learn how to find a verse on a page in the Bible.**

The title of the book is at the top of the page.

ISAIAH 40

8 Then said Hezekiah to Isaiah, Good is the
word of the LORD which thou hast spoken.
He said moreover, For there shall be peace
and truth in my days.

Chapter 40

Comfort ye, comfort ye my people, saith
your God.
2 Speak ye comfortably to Jerusalem, and
cry unto her that her warfare is accom-

and shall gently lead those that are with
young.
12 Who hath measured the waters in the hol-
low of his hand, and meted out heaven with
the span, and comprehended the dust of the
earth in a measure, and weighed the moun-
tains in scales, and the hills in a balance?
13 Who hath directed the Spirit of the
LORD, or being his counsellor hath taught
him?

Each chapter is labeled with the number of the chapter.

Each verse in the chapter has a number.

Practice it!

Use the page above to answer the questions.
Fill in the circle next to each correct answer.

1. What is the title of this book of the Bible?

   ○ Isaiah ○ Jeremiah

2. What is the number of the chapter?

   ○ 12 ○ 40

3. What is the number of the verse colored yellow?

   ○ 12 ○ 40

Bonus 4. What chapter is verse 8 from?

   ○ 39 ○ 40

God Is Bigger
Isaiah 40:12

Name ___________________________

David knew God would protect him.
God is bigger than Goliath.

God is bigger than any problems people have.
God wants all people to trust Him.

Isaiah 40:12 gives some word pictures
of how big God is.

Listen to Isaiah 40:12 and circle the four pictures described in the verse.

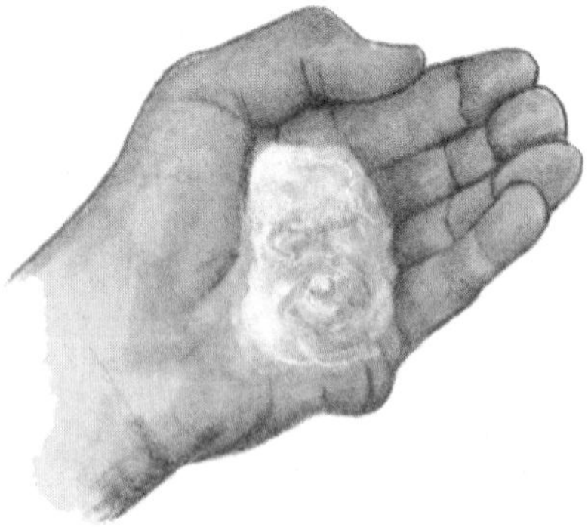

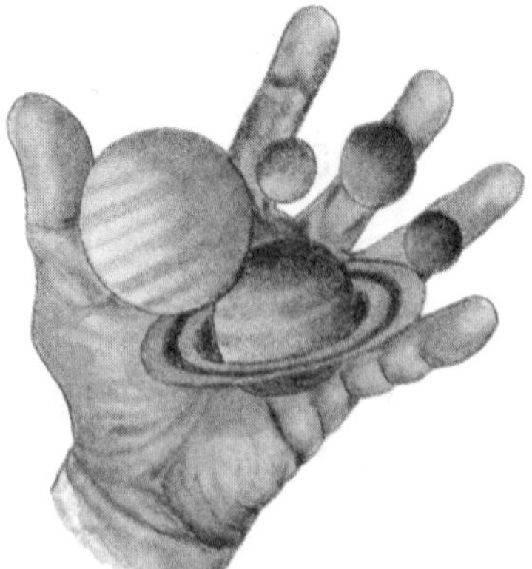

Saul Becomes Angry
I Samuel 18-20

Name ______________________________

At first, Saul loved David's courage.
But the people praised David more than Saul.

Fill in the circle next to the correct answer for each question.

1. How did Saul act after hearing the people praise David?
   - ○ Saul loved David more.
   - ○ Saul hated David.

2. What did Saul try to do with the spear?
   - ○ Saul tried to kill David.
   - ○ Saul tried to protect the palace.

3. To save his life, what did David do?
   - ○ David ran and hid.
   - ○ David fought with a spear.

4. How did Jonathan help David?
   - ○ Jonathan hid him in his room.
   - ○ Jonathan told David to run from Saul.

5. What promise did David and Jonathan make?
   - ○ They promised to always be friends.
   - ○ They promised to go to the palace together.

Best Friends

I John 4:7

Name ____________________

Jonathan was King Saul's son. Jonathan was not jealous because God had chosen David to be the next king. Jonathan cared for David's safety. Jonathan and David were best friends.

Word bank
help
love
share

Use a word from the word bank to finish the sentence under each picture. Finish the last sentence with your own words and draw your own picture.

Best friends ____________.

Best friends ____________ each other.

Best friends show ____________ to each other.

Best friends ____________ ____________.

Running from Saul
I Samuel 21-23

Name ______________________________

Use the words in the word bank to finish the sentences.

safe
God
kill

1. King Saul was jealous of David and wanted to ____________ him.

2. David trusted God to keep him ____________.

3. ____________ led David to safety from King Saul.

Start at the ★. Draw a line to help David find his way out of danger and to the city of Engedi. (Remember, never draw lines through walls.)

God kept David safe. God can keep me safe.

Engedi

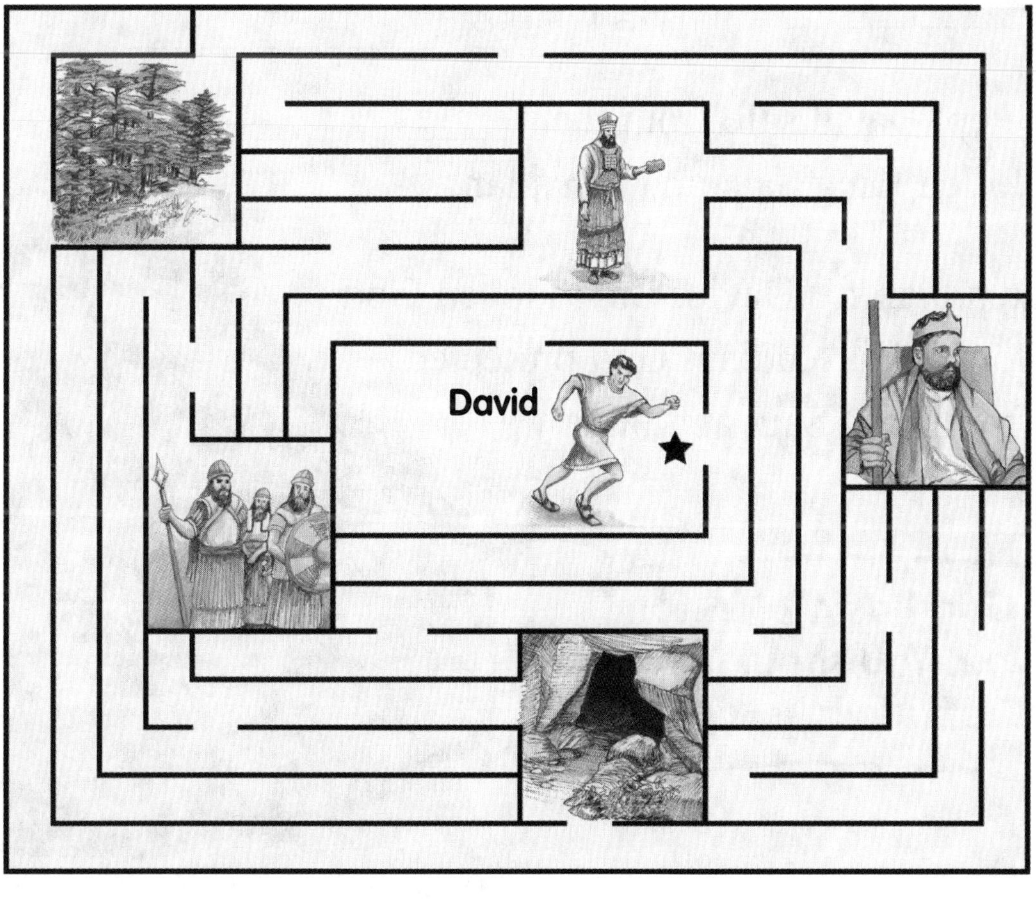
David
★

Safe with God
I Samuel 24, 26, 31

Name ______________________

King Saul wanted to kill David. But David never tried to kill Saul. David honored Saul because Saul was still king of the land.

Use the words in the word bank to finish the sentences.

battle
cave
jug
spear

1. God kept David safe when David was in the ______________ where King Saul was.

2. God kept David safe when David took King Saul's ______________ and water ______________ during the night.

3. God kept David safe from the ______________ that killed King Saul and Jonathan.

God had a plan for David. David loved God and followed His leading. God protected David from King Saul and other dangers.

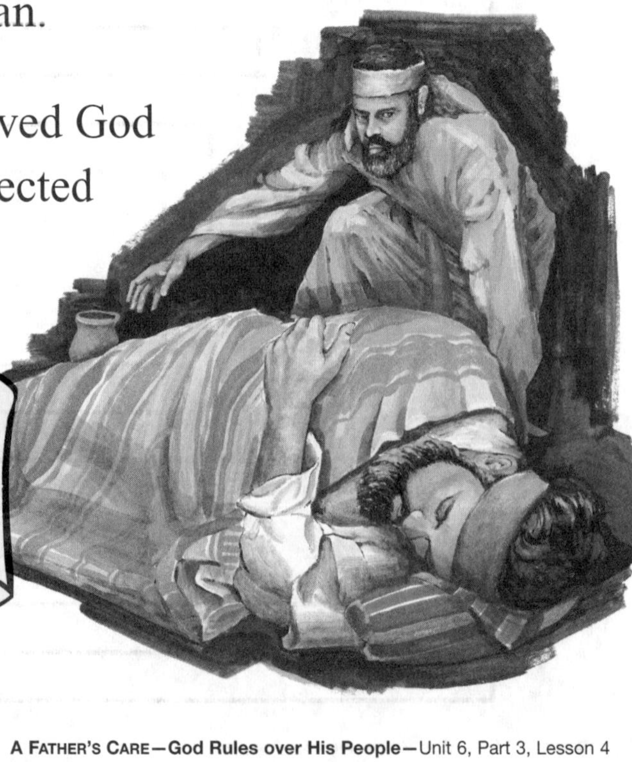

God has a plan for you. You should love and follow Him.

A Loving King
II Samuel 7:1-29; 9:1-13

Name ______________________

Circle the correct word in each box to finish the story.

God kept His promise. [David / Jonathan] became king after Saul died.

King David [hated / loved] God and wanted to build a beautiful place to worship Him.

God promised that David's [son / grandson] would build His temple.

David remembered his [love / hatred] for Jonathan.

He remembered his promise to always be Jonathan's [enemy / friend].

David found Jonathan's [son / daughter] and brought him to live in the palace.

A Wise King

I Kings 3:3-15; 5:1-5; 6:1-4

Name ______________________________

Solomon was King David's son. As God had promised, Solomon built the temple for the people to worship. Solomon loved God and asked God to help him be a good king.

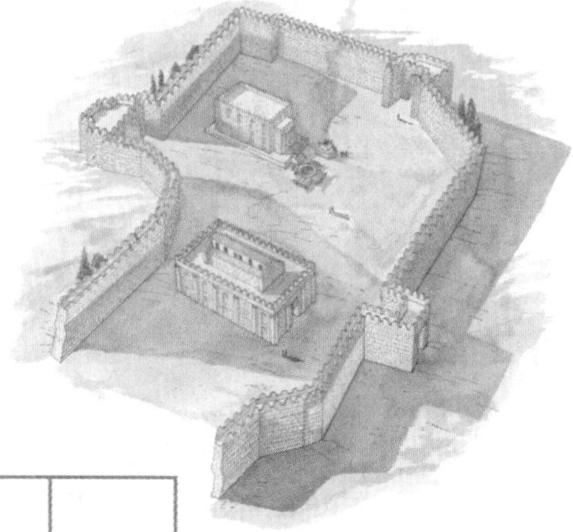

Use the code to finish the sentences.

d	e	h	i	l	o	r	s

Solomon asked God for w _ _ _ _ m.

God gave Solomon more than he asked.

God also gave Solomon _ _ c _ _ _,

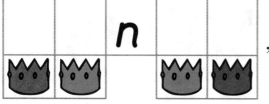

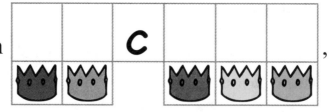

_ _ n _ _, and a long _ _ f _.

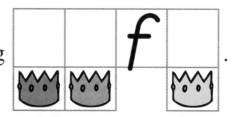

Serving like a King

Name ______________________________

Josiah was a king who loved God.

1. **Finish each sentence with your own words and sign the bottom.**
2. **Cut along the heavy line. Roll up like a scroll.**
3. **Secure with a sticker or ribbon and present to a parent.**

I can serve God like King Josiah.

Josiah served God when he was still a boy.

I can serve God by ______________________________
____.

Josiah cared for God's house.

I can care for God's house by ____________________
____.

Josiah showed his love for God by reading and obeying God's Word.

I can show my love for God by ____________________
____.

Serving like a king

I want to serve God like a king.

signed ______________________________

Serving like a King (continued)

A Young King

II Kings 22:1–23:25

Name ______________________________

Write the letter of the correct word from the word bank to finish each sentence.

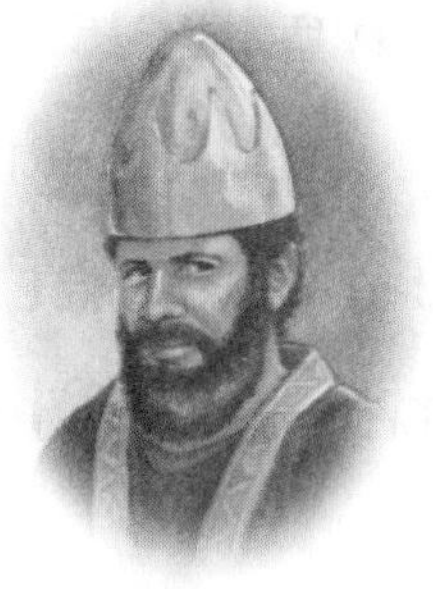

1. King _____ wanted to build a temple.
2. God let King _____ build it.
3. Many _____ after them did not love God or care for the temple.
4. The _____ became old and dirty.

A. Solomon
B. temple
C. David
D. kings

Use the words in the word bank to finish the puzzle.

eight | loved
obey | Word
workers

Across

1. King Josiah had _____ repair and clean the temple.
5. King Josiah _____ God.

Down

2. King Josiah chose to _____ God's Word.
3. Josiah became king when he was _____ years old.
4. The temple workers found a copy of God's _____.

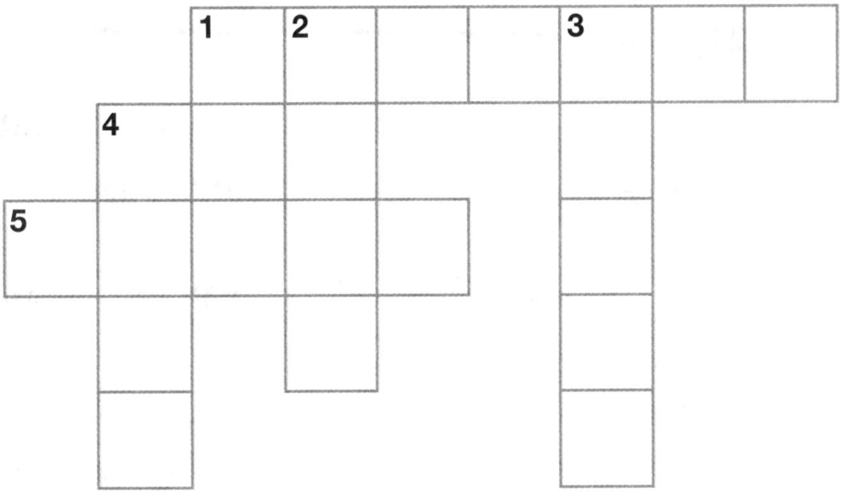
1
2
3
4
5

The Kings Write

Name ____________________

We have Bibles today because God used many men to write His Word. God told these men what to write. God used Moses to write five Old Testament books.

God also used two kings to write some of His books. King David wrote part of a book and King Solomon wrote three books.

God used the skills of David and Solomon as they wrote His Word.

Priest showing a scroll

Use the descriptions to help you know whom God used to write each book. Write *David* or *Solomon* next to the books each king wrote. *Note:* You will write Solomon's name two times.

David played the harp and loved music.
Solomon was given great wisdom by God.

____________ 1. **Proverbs** contains many wise verses from God.

____________ 2. The **Psalms** can be sung like songs.

____________ 3. **Ecclesiastes** wisely tells of the hope in trusting God.

John Baptizes Jesus

Matthew 3:1-17

Name ____________________

God chose John the Baptist to tell people about the coming Messiah. John was humble and obeyed God.

Put an *X* in the box of the correct words that finish each sentence.

1. John wore ____.
   - ☐ clothes made of camel's hair
   - ☐ a beautiful, colored coat

2. John baptized those who ____.
   - ☐ wanted to be baptized
   - ☐ repented of their sin

3. At first, John did not want to baptize Jesus because ____.
   - ☐ he felt unworthy and wanted Jesus to baptize him
   - ☐ he did not believe in Jesus

4. Jesus told John to baptize him so that ____.
   - ☐ God would give John His blessing
   - ☐ God's righteousness would be done

5. When Jesus was baptized, God said that He was ____.
   - ☐ very pleased with His Son, Jesus
   - ☐ very angry with John

Pleasing God
John 8:29

Name ______________________

John the Baptist pleased God. Jesus pleased God. They each did what was right.

Do you please God?

Do you do what is right?

Finish the face next to each picture.

Draw a smile if the action pleases God.

Draw a frown if the action does not please God.

FRUIT CHEWS
COOKIES
HYMNS

Temptation
Luke 4:1-15

Name ______________________________

The Devil tried to get Jesus to do something wrong. He tempted Jesus. Jesus did not sin. Jesus did what was right.

Mount of Temptation

On each blank, write *T* if the sentence is true or *F* if the sentence is false.

______ 1. Jesus went into the desert after He was baptized.

______ 2. Jesus did not eat anything for forty days.

______ 3. The Devil tried to get Jesus to worship him.

______ 4. Jesus did not know what to do.

______ 5. Jesus did not give in to the Devil's temptation.

Solve each addition problem.
Use the code to answer the question.

4 + 4 = ☐ I

6 + 6 = ☐ L

5 + 5 = ☐ E

3 + 3 = ☐ B

How did Jesus resist the Devil?
Jesus quoted verses from the

6	8	6	12	10

What Will You Do?

Name ______________________________

You might be tempted to do something wrong today. When it happens, what will you do? Will you do what is wrong, or will you be like Jesus and do what is right?

Read each story. Fill in the circle next to the correct answer.

Your mom tells you to clean your room after dinner. You want to go outside to play. Right after dinner, the phone rings, and your mom answers it. You know she won't see you if you sneak out the back door. You really want to play!

What should you do to please Jesus?

○ I should clean my room.

○ I should go outside and play.

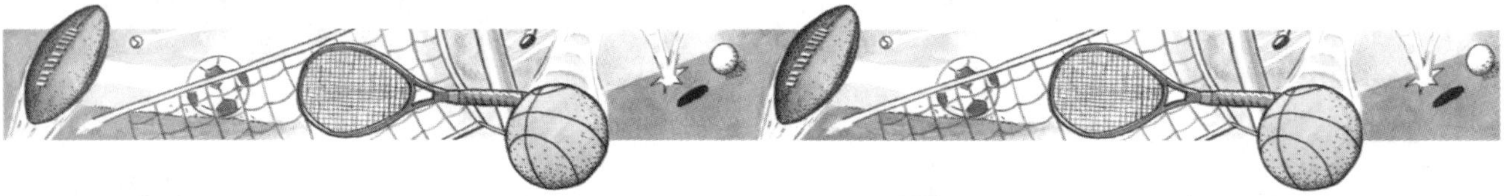

Your uncle gave you a new soccer ball for your birthday. Your friend wants to play with it. The last time you shared a toy with him, he lost it. You don't want anything to happen to your new soccer ball.

What should you do to please Jesus?

○ I should share my soccer ball with my friend.

○ I should hide my soccer ball from my friend.

The First Miracle

John 2:1-11

Name ____________________

Jesus and His disciples were invited to a wedding. When the servants ran out of wine for the guests to drink, Jesus helped them. He performed a miracle!

Match the questions with the pictures below.
Write the letter in the blank.

_____ 1. Who told Jesus that the servants ran out of wine?

_____ 2. Whom did Jesus tell to fill up the water pots?

_____ 3. What did the servants put into the water pots?

_____ 4. Who tasted the water and found it was wine?

_____ 5. Who performed the miracle?

A. Mary

B. water

C. Jesus

D. the main server

E. the servants

A Family Believes
John 4:46-54

Name ______________________________

An important man in Galilee needed help. He looked for Jesus. He knew that Jesus would help.

Use the words in the word bank to finish the sentences.

Jesus	son	family	heal

1. The man's ______________ was very sick.
2. The man believed that Jesus could ______________ his son.
3. ______________ healed the man's son.
4. All of the man's ______________ believed in Jesus and were saved.

This important man believed Jesus could help Him. The man and his family trusted Jesus for their salvation. Are you trusting Jesus?

A Fisher of Men

Luke 5:1-11

Name ____________________

Simon Peter was a fisherman. He spent his time catching fish. Peter left his boat and followed Jesus. Instead of catching fish, Peter told people about salvation through Jesus. He was now a "fisher of men."

Draw a picture of Peter as a fisherman.

Draw a picture of Peter as a "fisher of men."

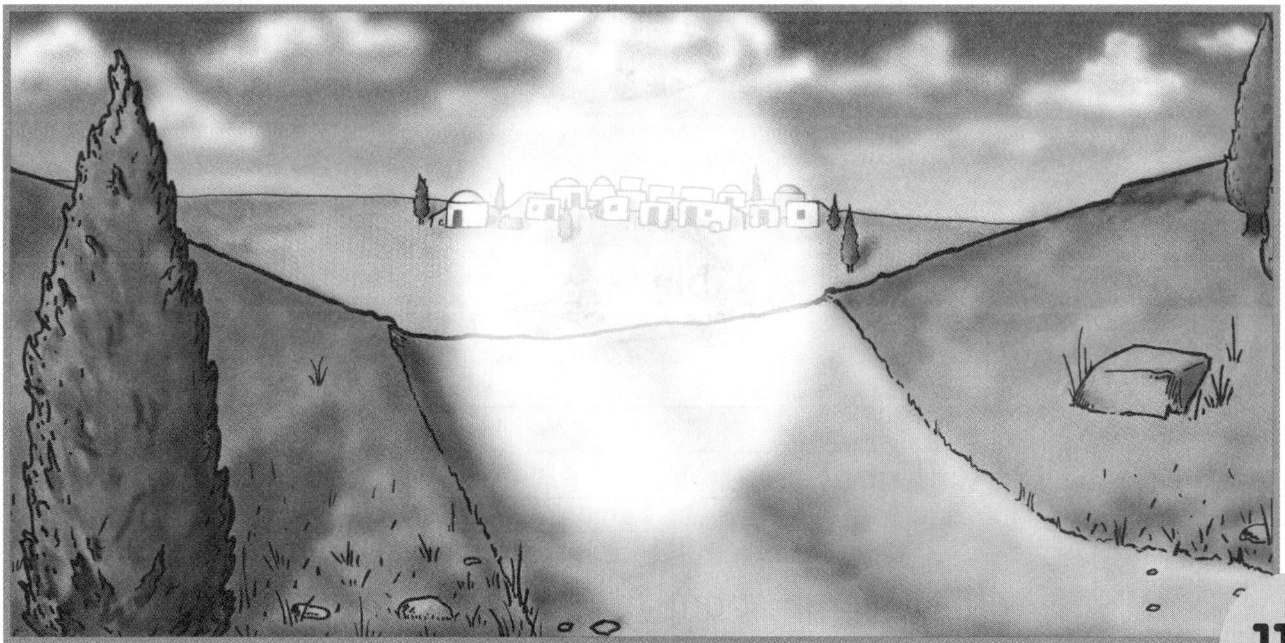

Fishing for Souls

Name ______________________

Do you love Jesus?
You can be a fisher of men like Peter!
Don't be afraid to be bold.
Tell other people that you love Jesus.

Cross out the fish with words that name a color.
Cross out the fish with words that begin with the letter *r*.
Circle the two fish that remain.
Write the remaining words to finish the sentence below.

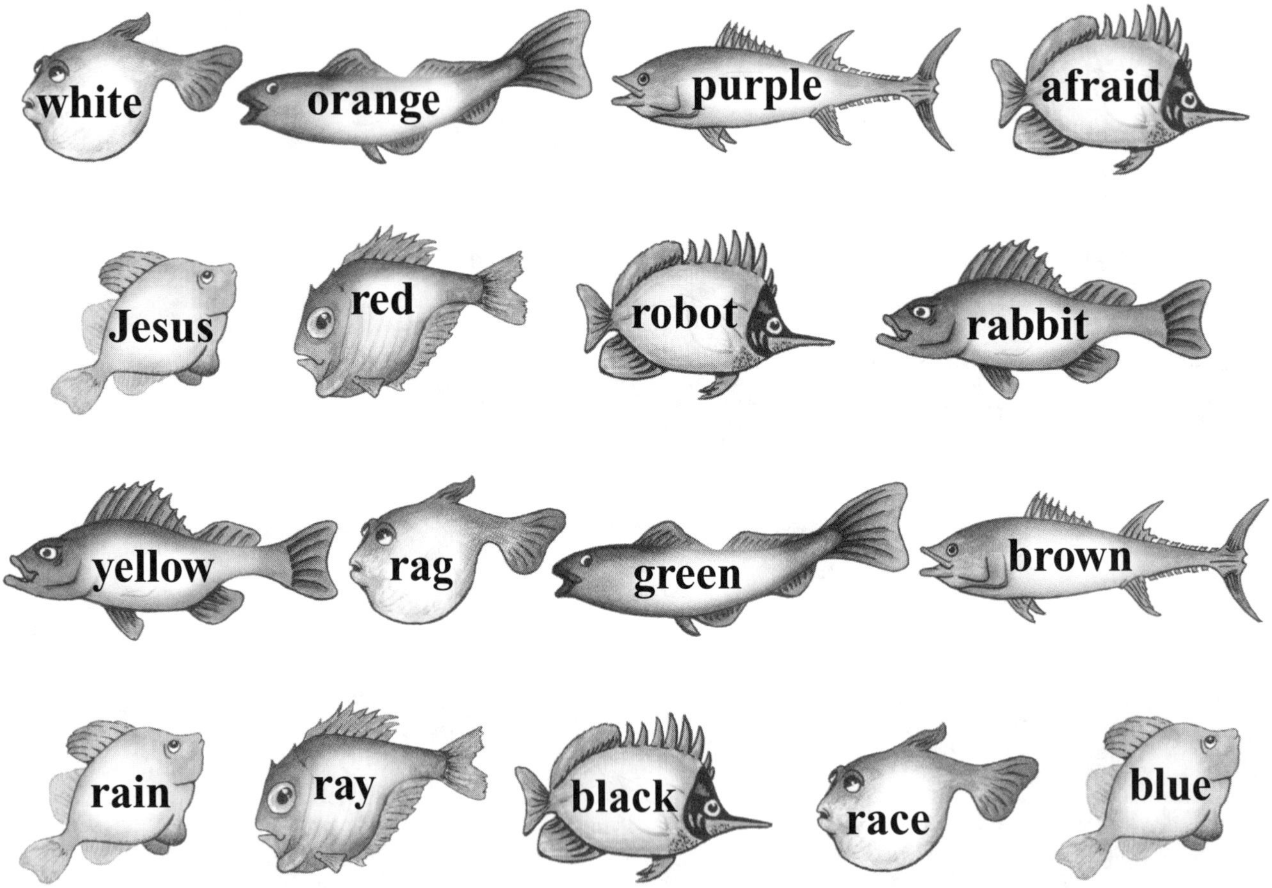

white
orange
purple
afraid
Jesus
red
robot
rabbit
yellow
rag
green
brown
rain
ray
black
race
blue

I will not be ________________ to tell

other people about ________________.

God Provides

Name ____________________

Jesus provided for Peter's needs. He gave Peter many fish. God knows what you need. He will provide for you!

Follow the directions on page 122 to make a reminder of God's provision for you.

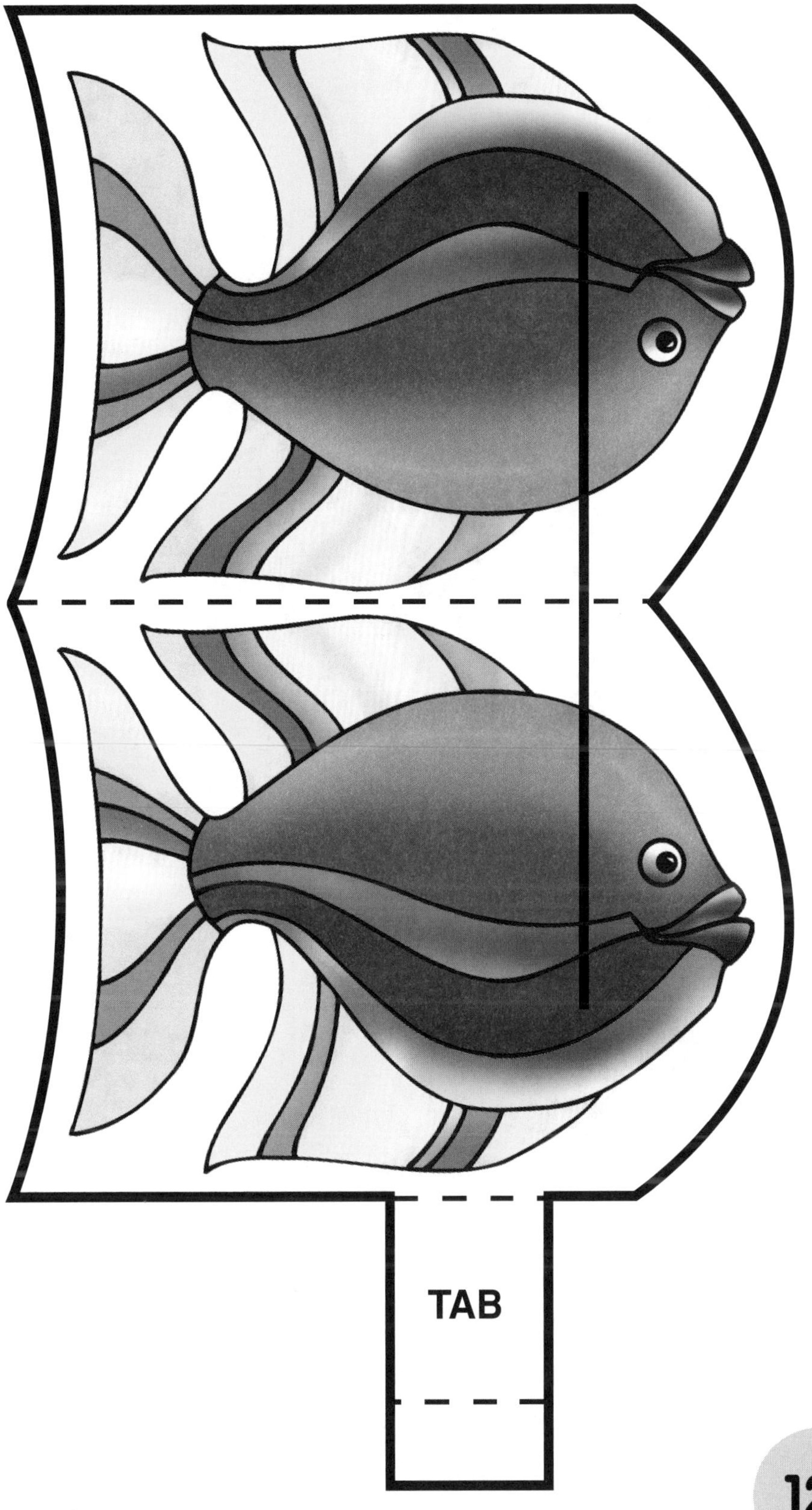
TAB

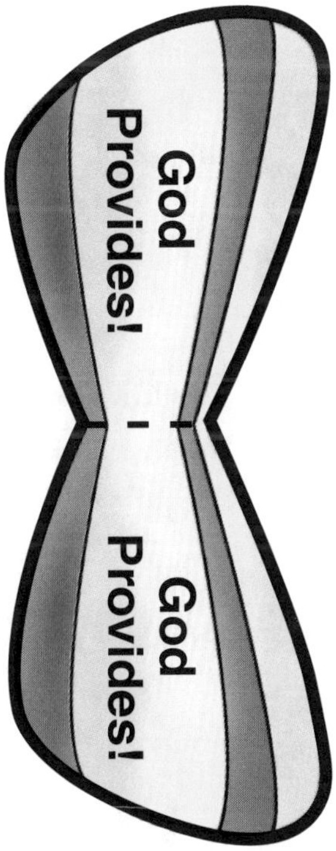
God Provides!
God Provides!

God Provides (continued)

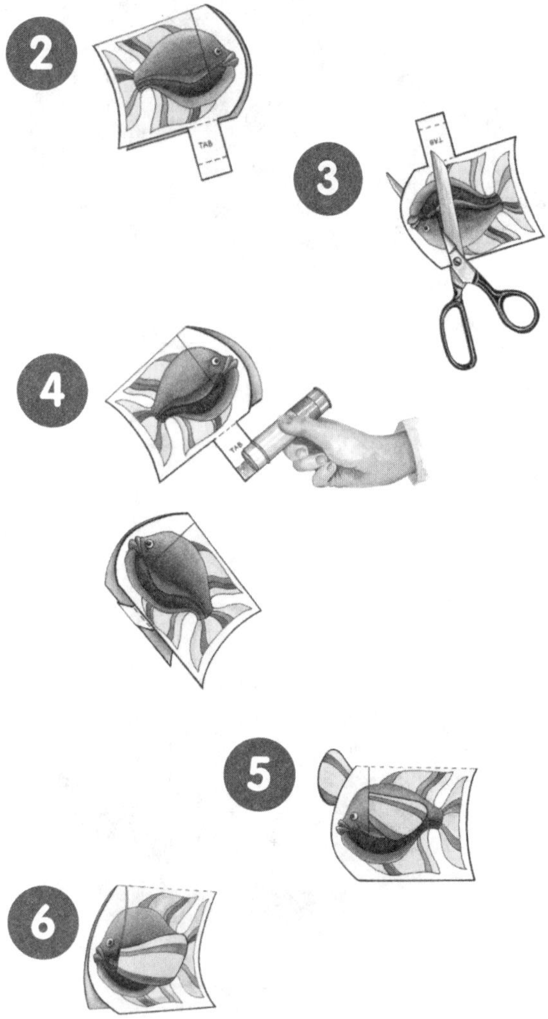
2
3
4
5
6

1. Cut out the patterns on the heavy lines.
2. Fold the tab and the fish on the dotted lines.
3. Cut a slit on the heavy line in the fish.
4. Glue the folded side of the tab to the fish as shown.
5. Slide the fin down into the slit on the fish.
6. Stand the fish on your desk as a reminder that God will provide for you.

Healing Faith
Mark 5:22-43

Name ______________________________

Jesus had the power to heal. Many people wanted Jesus to help them. Jesus healed those who had faith in Him.

Draw a line to match the first part of the sentence with the end of the sentence. Read each complete sentence.

1. Jairus was a synagogue ruler	from the dead.
2. The woman was healed because	who believed Jesus.
3. Jairus's daughter died before	Jesus arrived.
4. Jesus raised the girl	she had faith in Jesus.

When you have faith in Jesus, it means that you believe what He says. Do you know what Jesus says? Do you believe Him?

Color the speech bubbles that contain truths that Jesus taught.

- Love God with all your heart.
- I will never leave you.
- I came so you could be saved.
- I will do what pleases my Father.
- Fear not.
- I don't care about you.

Safe and Secure
Psalm 4:8

Name ______________________________

Use the code to fill in the letters in each answer.

Your friend is afraid of the dark and has trouble sleeping at night. You know that he loves Jesus. What can you say to help him?

"You don't need to be afraid to go to

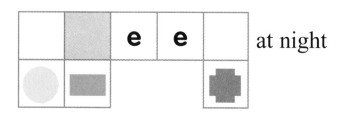

		e	e	

at night

because the

L			

will keep you

			e

!"

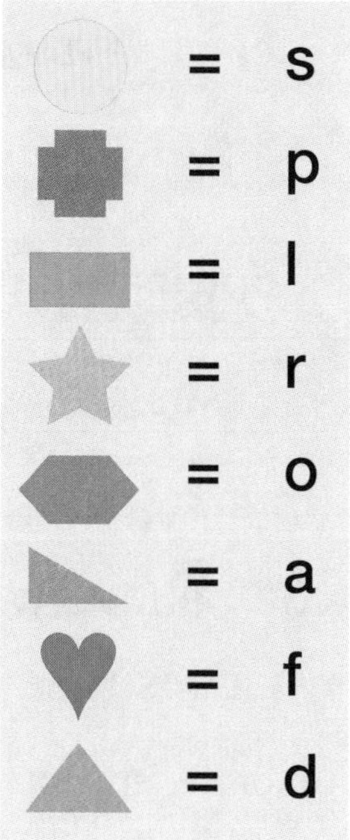

= s
= p
= l
= r
= o
= a
= f
= d

How do you know God will do what He says?

Write the letters from the colored boxes above into the boxes with matching colors below to finish the sentence.

God will do what He says because He is

		i	t	h		u	

!

Walking on Water
Matthew 14:21-33

Name ______________________

The disciples were in a boat on the Sea of Galilee. A storm came and they were afraid. The disciples saw Jesus coming, and they were afraid. Peter started to sink and he was afraid.

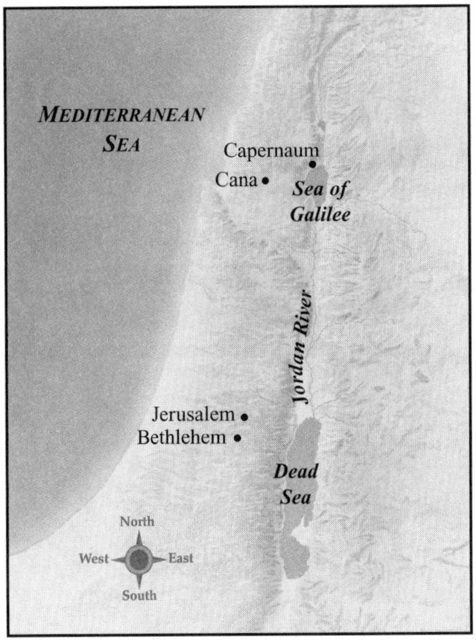
MEDITERRANEAN SEA
Capernaum
Cana
Sea of Galilee
Jordan River
Jerusalem
Bethlehem
Dead Sea
North
West
East
South

Write the letter of the correct word from the word bank to finish each sentence.

1. Jesus ____ on the water.
2. Peter started to sink in the water when he ____ away from Jesus.
3. Jesus ____ the storm.
4. The disciples ____ Jesus.

A. calmed
B. worshiped
C. walked
D. looked

Have you ever felt afraid?
God knows that people feel fear sometimes.
God has made a wonderful promise to His children!

Start at the ★ and write the words in order as you follow the word wheel.

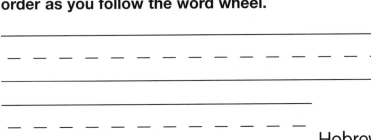

God
is
always
with
me.

____

____

______________________________ Hebrews 13:5

Every Little Thing

Name ____________________

God wants you to talk to Him about everything! He wants you to know that He loves you and cares about what happens to you.

Color the puzzle and discover how you can talk with God.

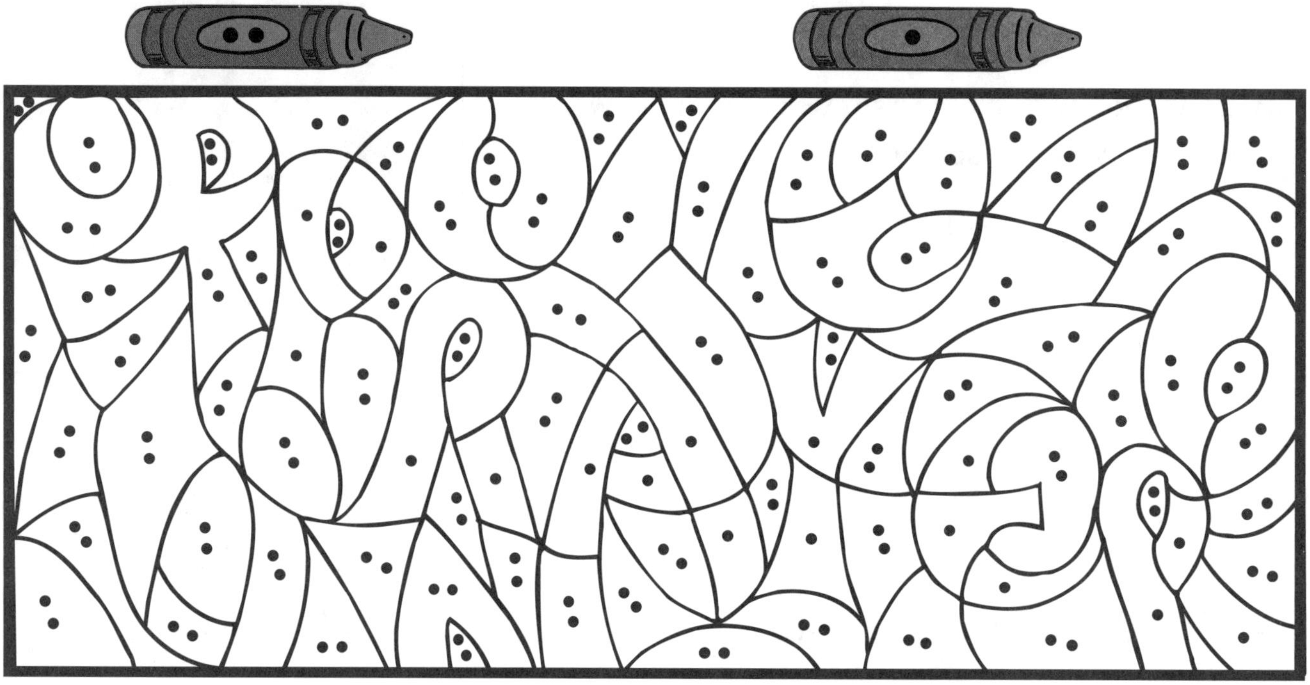

Color the boxes about your prayers.

- green — **Thank you.**
- purple — **Help me.**
- yellow — **I am sorry.**
- orange — **Please help them.**

Thank you for giving me good food to eat.	**Please help me to obey my parents.**
Please forgive me for being selfish.	**Please keep the missionaries safe.**

The Good Neighbor

Luke 10:25-37

Name ____________________

Jesus told the lawyer to love God and his neighbor.
Do you love God?
Do you love your neighbors?

Use the words in the word bank to finish the puzzle.

Thieves	neighbor	priest
Levite	Samaritan	money

Across

3. The Samaritan gave the inn keeper ____ to take care of the hurt man.
5. ____ robbed a man and beat him up.
6. The ____ man had compassion for the dying man.

Down

1. Jesus told a story about being a good ____.
2. The ____ saw the hurt man and went to the other side of the road.
4. The ____ looked at the man, but did not help him.

1
2
3
4
5
6
n e i g h b o
S a m a r i t a n

The Faith to See
Luke 18:35-43

Name ______________________

The blind man believed in Jesus.
Jesus answered the blind man's request.
Jesus healed the blind man.

Write the letter of the correct word from the word bank to finish each sentence.

A. understand
B. die
C. disciples

1. Jesus told His ____ what was going to happen to Him.
2. Jesus said He was going to suffer and ____.
3. The disciples did not ____ what Jesus meant.

Fill in the circle next to the correct answer.

1. What was the blind man doing before Jesus healed him?
   - ○ begging for food
   - ○ playing a game
2. What did the blind man do after Jesus healed him?
   - ○ begged for food again
   - ○ rejoiced and praised God
3. Why did Jesus say He healed the blind man?
   - ○ because of the blind man's faith
   - ○ because of the blind man's money

Reading from the Bible
Table of Contents

Name ____________________

The first four books of the New Testament tell of the life of Jesus on earth.

Use the table of contents to answer the questions.

1. Find the first four books of the New Testament. Which is *not* one of them?
   - ○ Mark
   - ○ Luke
   - ○ Ephesians

2. The Bible tells of Jesus' walking on the water in John 6:14-29. On what page does John begin?
   - ○ 651
   - ○ 695
   - ○ 720

3. The Bible tells of Jesus healing the blind man in Luke 18:35-43. On what page does Luke begin?
   - ○ 589
   - ○ 625
   - ○ 670

Books of the Bible

Books of the Old Testament

	Page		Page
Genesis	1	Ecclesiastes	410
Exodus	32	Song of Solomon	415
Leviticus	59	Isaiah	417
Numbers	77	Jeremiah	456
Deuteronomy	106	Lamentations	501
Joshua	128	Ezekiel	504
Judges	144	Daniel	544
Ruth	160	Hosea	556
1 Samuel	162	Joel	561
2 Samuel	187	Amos	563
1 Kings	207	Obadiah	567
2 Kings	232	Jonah	568
1 Chronicles	256	Micah	569
2 Chronicles	278	Nahum	572
Ezra	303	Habakkuk	574
Nehemiah	310	Zephaniah	576
Esther	320	Haggai	578
Job	325	Zechariah	579
Psalms	346	Malachi	586
Proverbs	394		

Books of the New Testament

	Page		Page
Matthew	589	1 Timothy	737
Mark	609	2 Timothy	740
Luke	625	Titus	742
John	651	Philemon	743
Acts	670	Hebrews	744
Romans	695	James	750
1 Corinthians	704	1 Peter	753
2 Corinthians	714	2 Peter	756
Galatians	720	1 John	758
Ephesians	723	2 John	761
Philippians	727	3 John	761
Colossians	730	Jude	762
1 Thessalonians	733	Revelation	763
2 Thessalonians	735		

Never Too Busy

Matthew 18:1-10; Mark 10:13-16

Name ____________________

Jesus is never too busy to care about children. He cares about you!

Who said these words?

Write the speaker underneath the words.

Jesus mothers disciples

1. **Please bless our children!**

____

2. **Do not send the children away!**

____

3. **Go away! Jesus is too busy!**

____

4. **Bring the children to Me!**

____

The disciples wanted to know who would be the greatest in heaven. Jesus told them what to do.

Cross out the letters *i, s,* and *c.* Write the remaining letters in order to finish the sentence.

5. Jesus told them to be ____________________.

s i h c s i u m i c s b s i c l c s e c

Loving Others

I John 4:21

Name ____________________

Jesus loves you very much. He wants you to show love to others. Do you show love?

Are these children showing love to others?
Read each sentence and color the correct heart.

	Did not show love	Showed love
1. Dmitri let Sam go first in line.	♡	♡
2. Keli ran to play and did not help her mom carry the groceries in.	♡	♡
3. Tarah invited Nari to church.	♡	♡
4. Megan shared her crayons with her new friend.	♡	♡
5. Brock slammed the door while his brother was sleeping.	♡	♡

What can you do to show love for others?

Finish the sentence.

6. I can show love by ____________________
____

You Are Special!

Name ______________________________

Children are important to Jesus. You are important to Jesus! He made you different from everybody else! He loves you very much.

Tell how God made you special by finishing the sentences.

I Am Special!

I have ______________ hair. I have ______________ eyes.

My birthday is ______________________________.

I like to eat ____________________________.

My favorite game is ______________________.

Color the boxes that say something true about you.

I like to share my toys!	I like to go to church!	I like to be kind to others!
I like to sing!	I like to obey!	

Hosanna

Matthew 21:1-11, 15-16

Name ______________________

Jesus rode into Jerusalem. Some people shouted praises. Other people did not believe in Him.

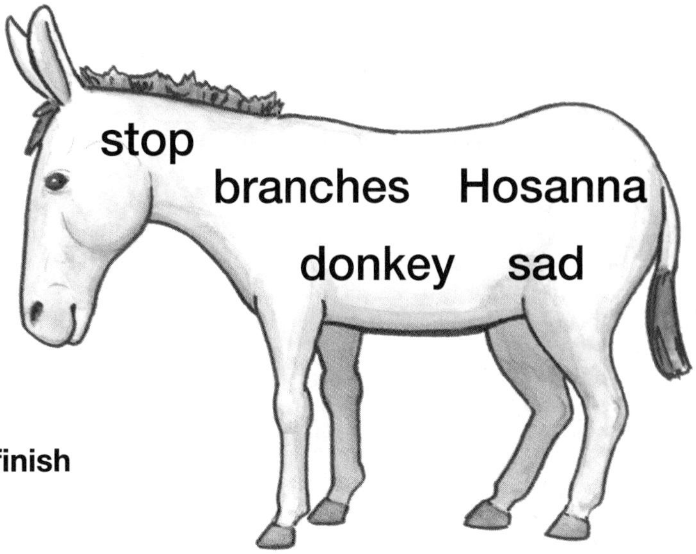
stop
branches
Hosanna
donkey
sad

Use the words from the word bank to finish the sentences.

1. Jesus rode a ______________ into Jerusalem.
2. The people put ______________ on the road.
3. The people shouted, "______________".
4. The Pharisees wanted the people to ______________ praising Jesus.
5. Jesus was ______________ because some people did not believe in Him.

God's House
Mark 11:15-19

Name ____________________

Draw a line to the correct ending for each sentence.

1. Jesus came to the temple each day	because the temple was to be clean and holy for worship.
2. Jesus sent out those who cheated and sold things in the temple	because they were angry with what Jesus did and said.
3. The religious leaders looked for ways to destroy Jesus	because He wanted to teach the people and heal the sick.

Circle the things that belong in a church.

HYMNAL

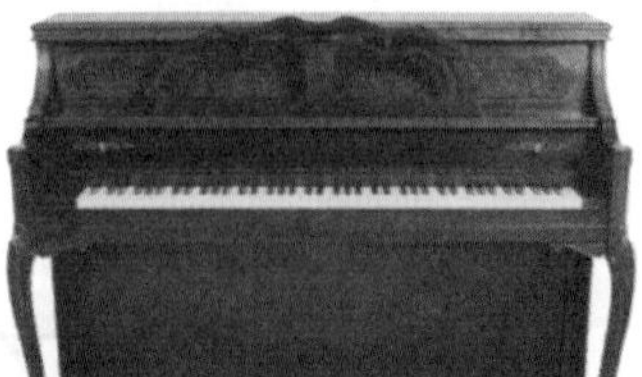

The Last Supper
Mark 14:12-26

Name ______________________________

Jesus and His disciples ate together.
After they ate, Jesus washed their feet.

Write the letters of the words that correctly finish the sentences.

A. someone
B. servant
C. Passover
D. argued

1. Jesus and the disciples were in Jerusalem to celebrate the _____.
2. Some disciples _____ about who would be first.
3. Jesus showed them how to be a _____.
4. Jesus said _____ would betray Him.

Color the bowl beside the ways you can serve others.

- let others have first choice
- take the biggest piece
- play with your baby brother or sister
- do your chores
- be kind to others
- always go first

God's Gift

John 3:16

Name ______________________

Because Adam and Eve chose to sin, every person is born with sin. God gave His Son to make a way for people to go to heaven.

Circle the correct word to finish each sentence.

1. God ______ every person.

   hates loves

2. Jesus is God's ______.

   Son Father

3. God sent ______ to be the Savior.

   Jesus Adam

4. Trusting Jesus as the Savior gives eternal ______.

   life death

Color the puzzle to finish the sentence.

Jesus is God's ______ to us.

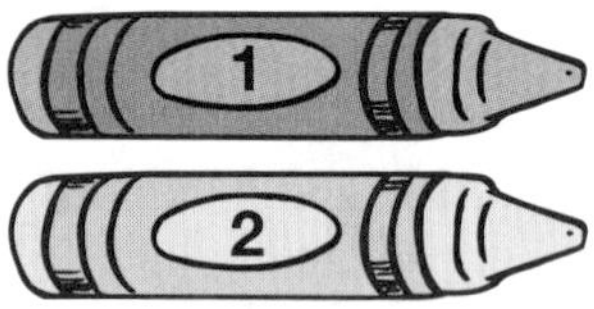
1
2

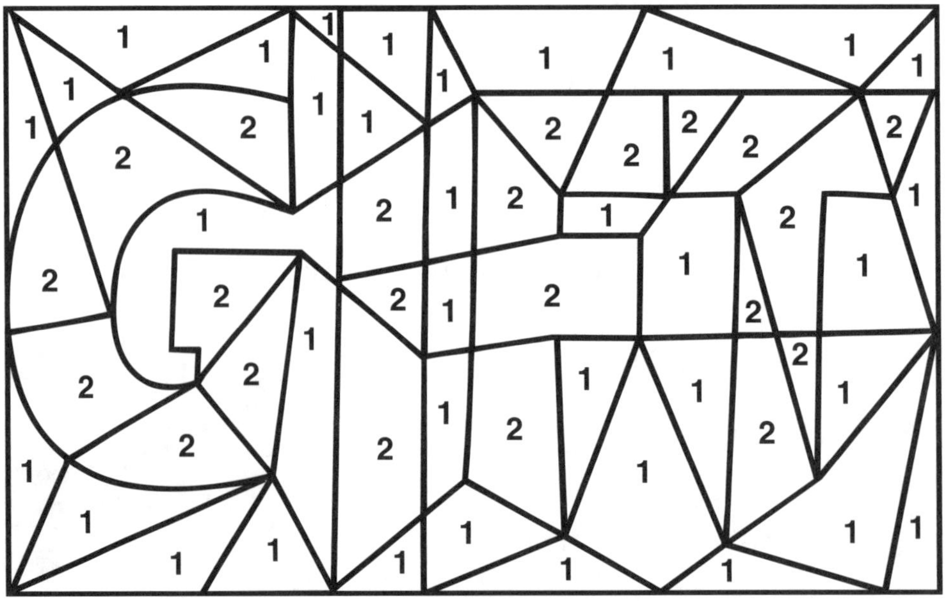

Reading from the Bible
References

Name ______________________

Remember the three parts of a reference: book, chapter, and verse

Draw a blue box around the name of each *book*.
Draw a red line under the number of each *chapter*.
Draw a yellow circle around the number of each *verse*.

1. Isaiah 63:9
2. Matthew 21:9
3. I Corinthians 15:4

Write the reference for each verse.

4. Luke, chapter ten, verse two
____

5. John, chapter twenty, verse nine
____

Write the reference of your memory verse.

____

God Is Everywhere
Psalm 139:1-10

Name ______________________

The Bible says God is everywhere and knows all things.

Draw a line from each sentence to the correct picture.

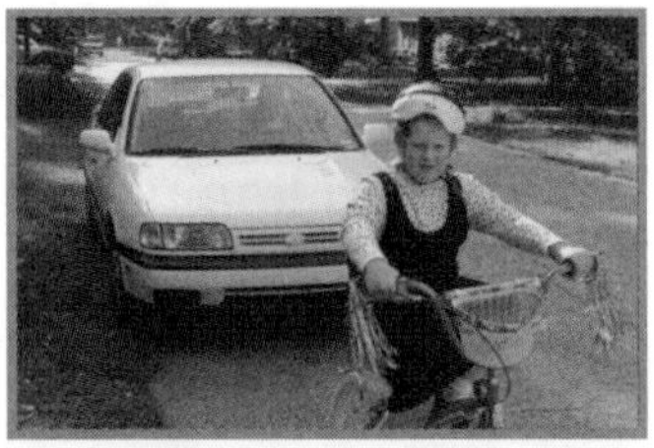

1. God sees when you sit.

2. God sees when you get up.

3. God sees when you sleep.

4. God knows what you say.

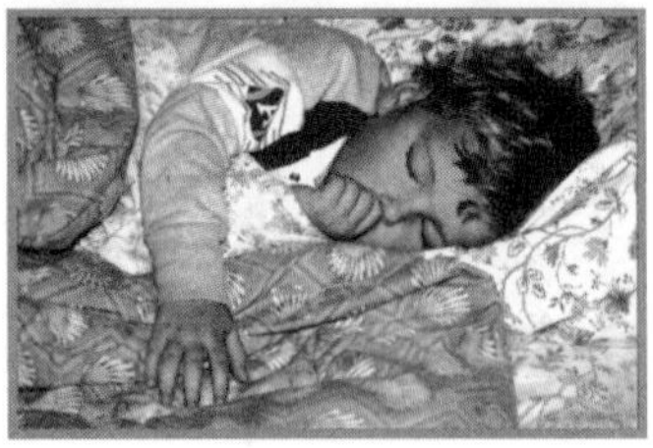

5. God knows when you are in danger.

Finish the sentence.

I obey God because ______________________.

Jesus Died for Us

Matthew 26:36–27:61

Name ____________________

Jesus went to the garden. Some disciples also went. The religious leaders falsely accused Jesus.

Finish the puzzle with words from the word bank. Write all the answers across.

pray	Pilate	Jesus
soldiers	Judas	One

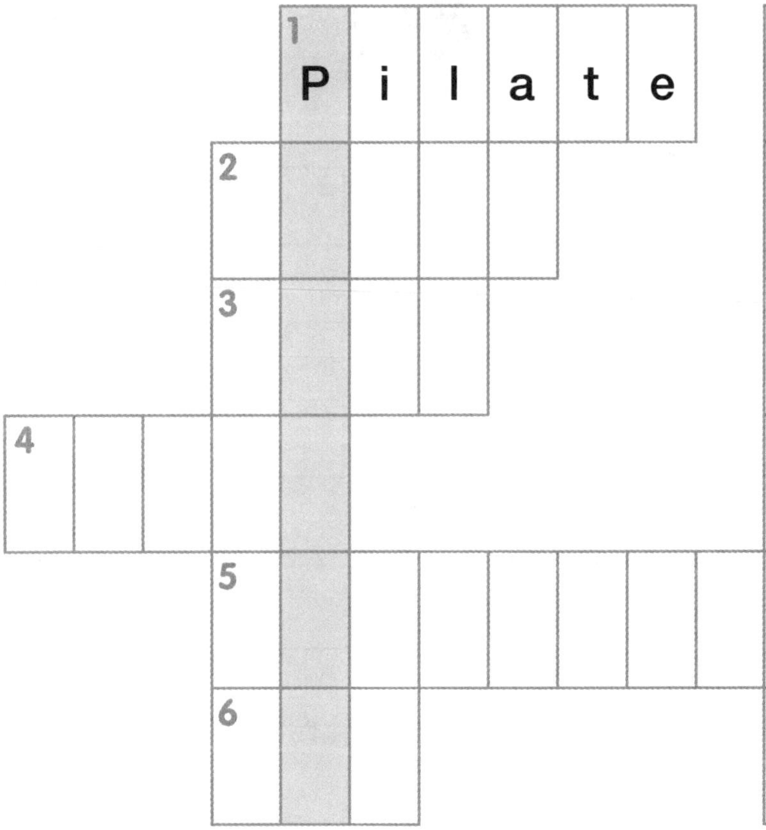

1 P i l a t e
2
3
4
5
6

1. ____ found nothing wrong with Jesus.
2. ____ died to save us.
3. Jesus was in the garden to ____.
4. ____ betrayed Jesus.
5. The ____ came to arrest Jesus.
6. ____ thief believed Jesus is the Savior.

Use the letters in the blue boxes in the puzzle to finish the sentence.

Jesus died for the sin of every ______.

Jesus Lives
John 19:38–20:18

Name ______________________

A friend buried Jesus' body. The women went to the tomb. An angel was there. The body of Jesus was gone! He had risen!

Use words from the word banks to finish the puzzles.

tomb
stood
open

Across

1. Soldiers ____ by the tomb.

Down

2. The women went to the ____.
3. The tomb was ____.

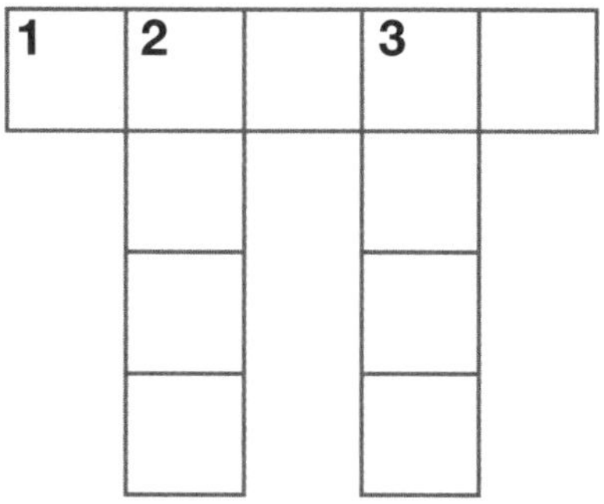
1
2
3

angel
alive
garden
ran

Across

1. The woman saw an ____.
3. Some disciples ____ to the tomb.
4. Jesus was ____.

Down

2. The tomb was in a ____.

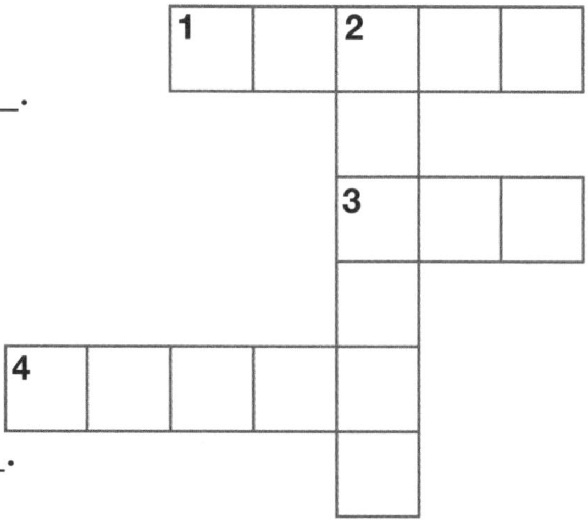
1
2
3
4

Jesus Returns to Heaven

Luke 24:13-53

Name ______________________________

Jesus rose from the dead. He appeared to His disciples. He was on earth forty days teaching the people. Jesus returned to His home in heaven.

Write some words that tell about heaven.

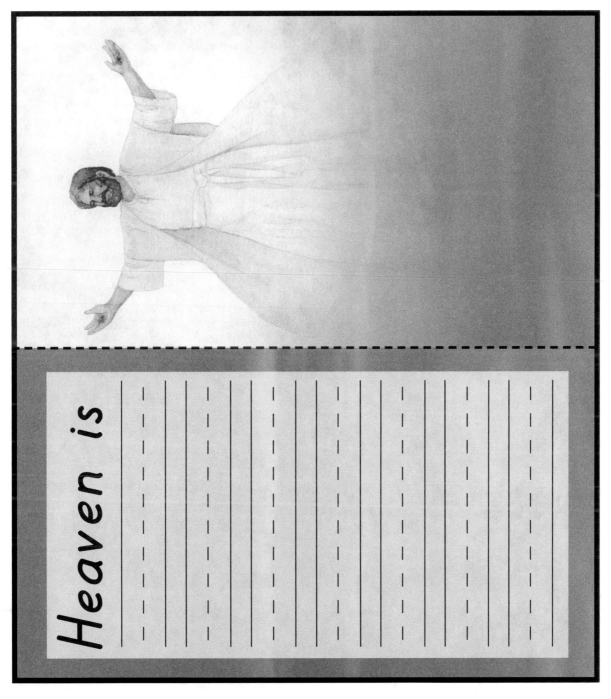

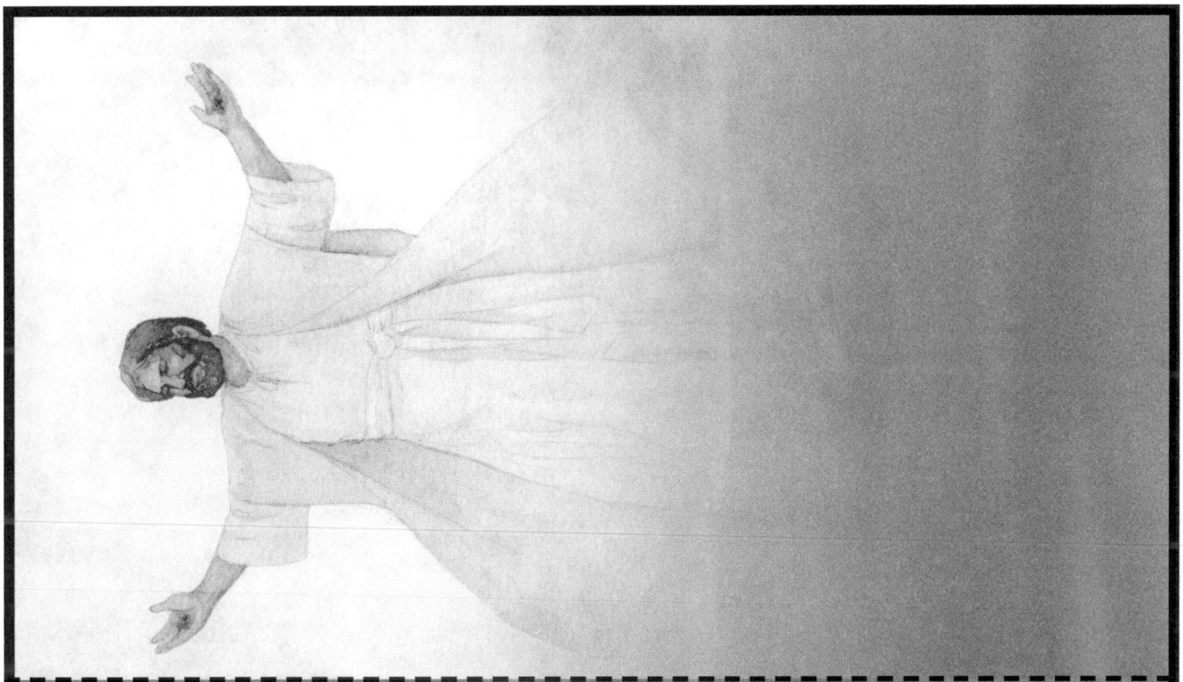

Heaven is

Jesus Returns to Heaven (continued)

Cut along the heavy outside line.
Fold on the dotted line so your words are on the inside.
Use your card to tell someone about the home in heaven that God has for believers.

Read more
about Jesus' promise
of a home in heaven
in John 14:1-6.
I would like
to tell you about
HEAVEN

The Cross

Name ______________________________

Jesus came to die for our sins. He wants to be our Savior. We should tell others about Him.

1. Cut the square along the outside lines.
2. Place the square with the pictures facing up.
3. Fold the pictures back along the dotted lines.
4. Turn the paper over. What do you see?
5. Use your cross to tell others about Jesus.

The Cross (continued)

The Lame Man
Acts 3–4:31

Name ______________________________

Peter and John spread the news that Jesus saves. They worked some miracles. The miracles helped the people listen to them.

Circle the picture that answers each question.

1. Where did Peter and John go?

2. Who was near the gate?

3. What did Peter say he could not give the man?

4. What did Peter do for the man?

5. What did the lame man do after he could walk again?

Saul Sees the Light

Acts 9:1-19*a*

Name ______________________

Saul hated Christians. Saul listened when God spoke to him. Saul was changed. Now he believed that Jesus Christ came to save.

Use the words in the word bank to finish the sentences.

light	baptized
Saul	obeyed
see	fell

1. ______________ went to Damascus to arrest believers.

2. A bright ______________ shone around him.

3. Saul ______________ to the ground.

4. Jesus spoke to Saul; then Saul could not ________.

5. Ananias ______________ God and helped Saul see.

6. Saul believed and was ______________.

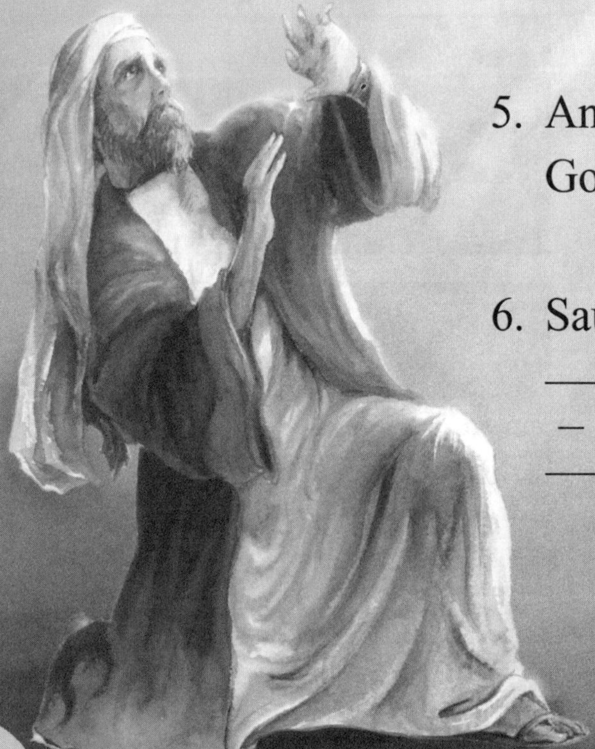

Speak for Jesus
II Timothy 1:7-8*a*

Name ______________________________

Peter and John told others about Jesus. You can tell others about Him too.

Color the Bible by the sentence if it is a way you can tell others about Jesus.

1. Give a tract to the checkout person at a store.

2. Tell someone you love him and care about his salvation.

3. Be a testimony to neighbors through your good behavior and friendliness.

4. Talk to your friends instead of listening to the Bible lesson.

5. Invite a friend to go with you to church or Bible club.

Scared or Brave?

Name ____________________

Our Savior is great. He will take care of us.
Jesus wants us to be brave.

Color the flag if the child was brave.

The thunder was loud. The lightning lit up Todd's room. He prayed that the Lord would care for him.

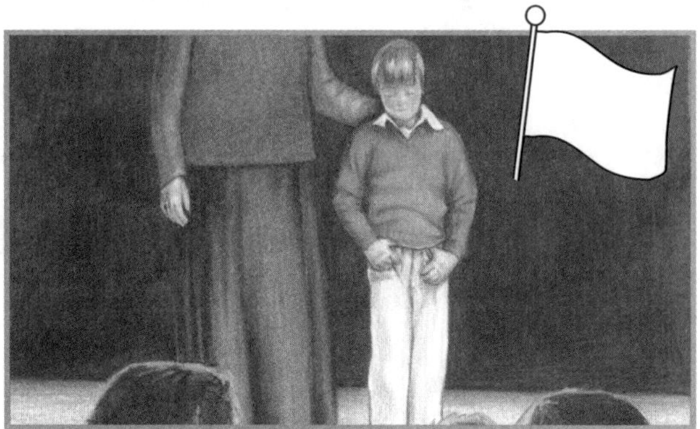

Bob had a part in the chapel program. When it was time for him to say his part, he hung his head. He did not say his part.

It was the first day of school, and Rob was going to a new school. He did not know any of the boys and girls. He prayed for a friend.

Nell was at the tire store with her dad. When she turned around she did not see Dad. Nell asked for help.

The Basket
Acts 9:19*b*-30

Name ____________________

Saul was happy to be a Christian. He began to preach. Some people wanted to kill Saul. They watched the city gates. Saul's new friends helped him escape over the wall.

Begin at the star and connect the dots counting by 5s to find what Saul used to escape over the wall.

Finish coloring the picture.

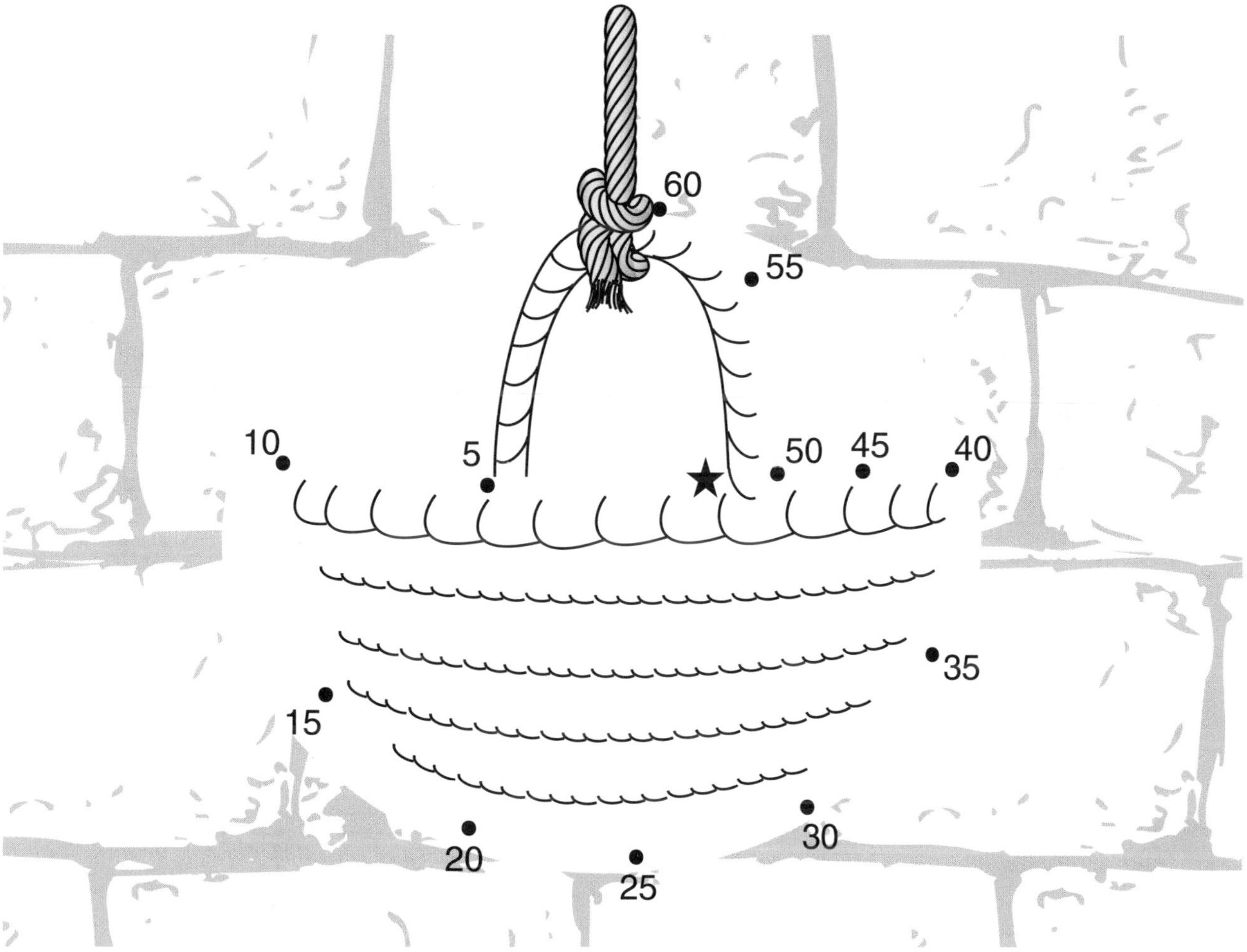
60
55
10
5
50
45
40
35
15
30
20
25

Will everyone like you if you are a Christian?

Food from Heaven

Acts 10

Name ______________________

Cornelius and his friends did not know how to be saved. They were Gentiles. God sent Peter to tell them. They became true believers.

Draw a line from each speaker to the correct speech bubble.

Angel

God

Peter

Cornelius

Cornelius' messengers

Eat these foods.

Cornelius, God heard your prayer.

We were sent to get you.

Tell me about God.

Jesus died for you.

A Friend

Name ____________________________

The Bible teaches us to be kind to others. Friends are a blessing from the Lord.

Draw a smile on the face beside each sentence that describes a way to be kind to someone who is new at school or church.

1	Introduce yourself to the new person.	
2	Ignore the new person.	
3	Show the new person the important places and things.	
4	Let the new person play alone.	
5	Invite the new person to eat with you.	

Jesus Loves the Children

Name ____________________________

Anyone can be saved. Children all over the world need to hear about Jesus. They need missionaries to share the gospel with them.

Cut out the pictures at the bottom of the page. Glue the pictures of the children to their continents.

Europe

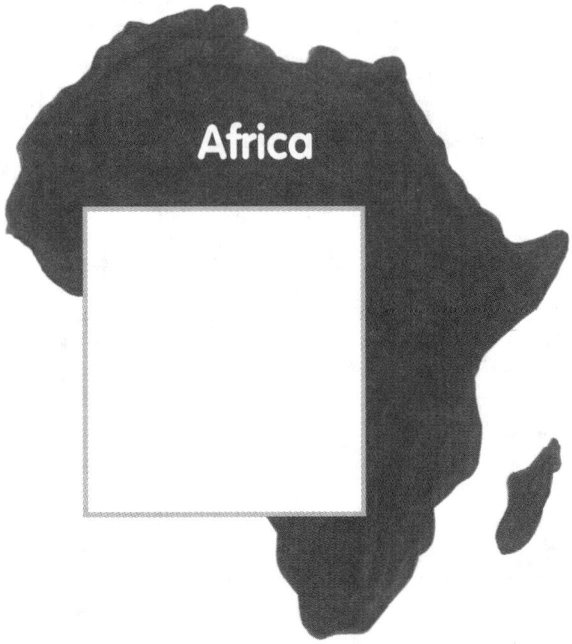
Africa

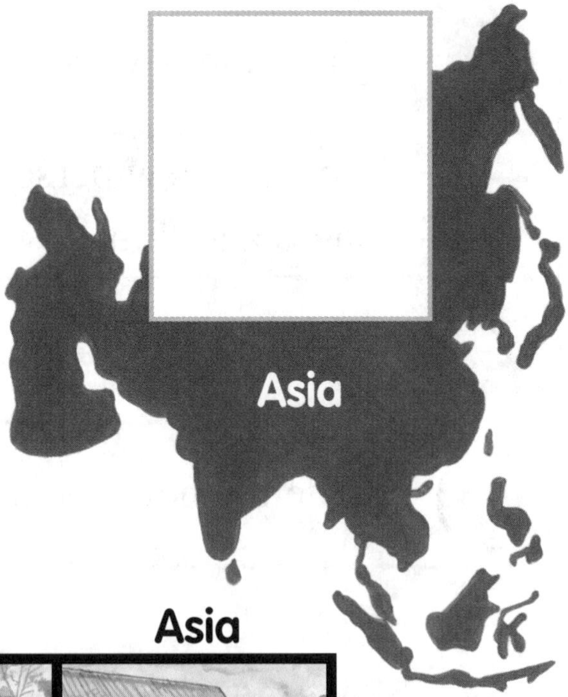
Asia

Europe
Africa
Asia

Answered Prayer

Acts 12:1-19

Name ______________________________

Peter was in prison. His friends met to pray for him. God answered their prayers.

Fill in the circle of each correct answer.

1. Who put Peter in prison?

   ○ King Herod ○ King David

2. Why was Peter in prison?

   ○ for not believing in Jesus ○ for preaching about Jesus

3. What were other Christians doing while Peter was in prison?

   ○ planning for Peter's escape ○ praying for Peter

4. Whom did God send to help Peter escape?

   ○ an angel ○ John

5. Who answered the door when Peter knocked?

   ○ Rhoda ○ Mary

6. How did the people react to Peter's arrival?

   ○ sad ○ surprised

Paul's First Journey
Acts 13-14

Name ______________________________

The Lord wanted Paul and Barnabas to be missionaries. They traveled to many cities. First they preached to the Jews in each city. Next they preached to the Gentiles. Some people believed; others did not.

People who cannot see learn to read by touching raised dots called Braille.

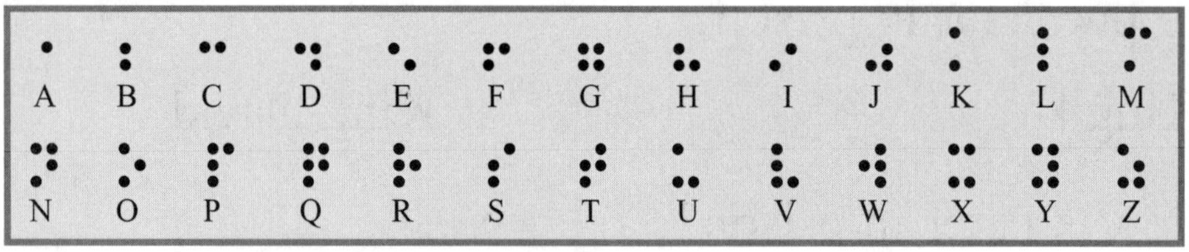
A B C D E F G H I J K L M
N O P Q R S T U V W X Y Z

Find the answers by using the Braille Code.

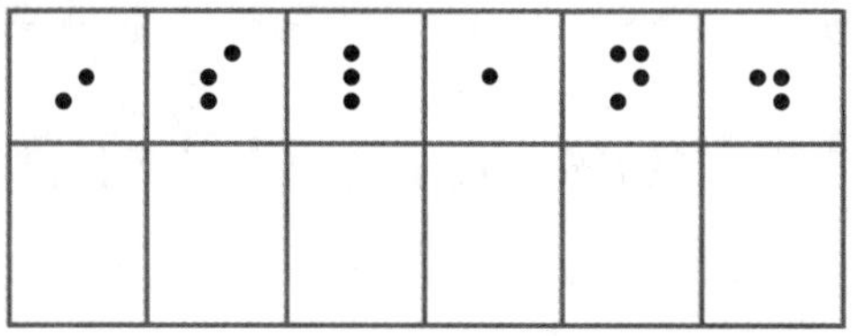

1. They went to the ______ of Cyprus.

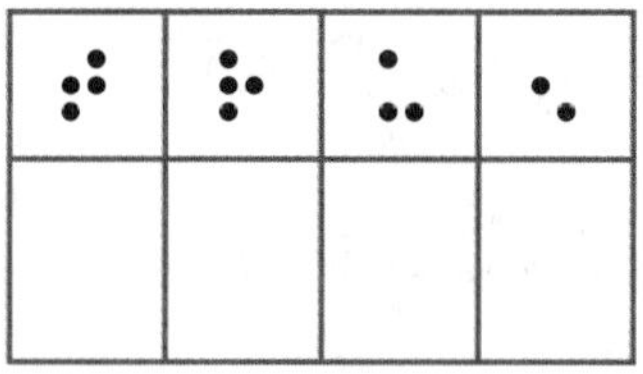

2. Elymas taught things that were not ______.

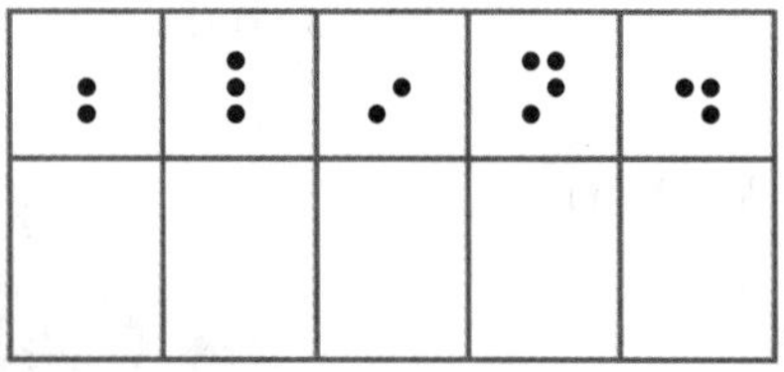

3. Elymas became ______.

4. Sergius Paulus saw the truth and believed on

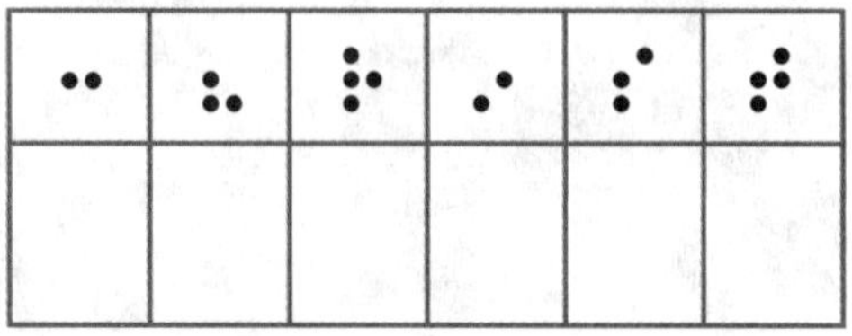

______.

Try writing your name using the Braille code.

Go and Tell
Romans 10:14

Name ______________________

Boys and girls everywhere need to hear about Jesus. They cannot be saved until they hear. Missionaries go to other lands to tell about Jesus.

Do you know what it would be like to go to another country?

Use the words in the word bank to finish the sentences about missionaries.

Bible
foods
obey
friends
new
ways

1. A missionary may need to learn a ______________ language.
2. A missionary may need to eat different ______________.
3. A missionary may learn new ______________ to do things.
4. A missionary will leave his old ______________ at home.
5. A missionary must know the ______________ well.
6. A missionary must ______________ the Lord.

Trust God

Name ______________________________

Sometimes we go through hard times. Maybe someone in your family is sick. Maybe there isn't enough money for things that you need. Someone you love may not be saved. God wants you to trust Him and depend on Him.

Is something hard happening to you now? Use your hand as a reminder to trust God. First pray, then look at your hand. Remember that *trust* has five letters—one for each finger of your hand.

Color the hand prayer reminder. Write the letters of *trust* on the fingers.

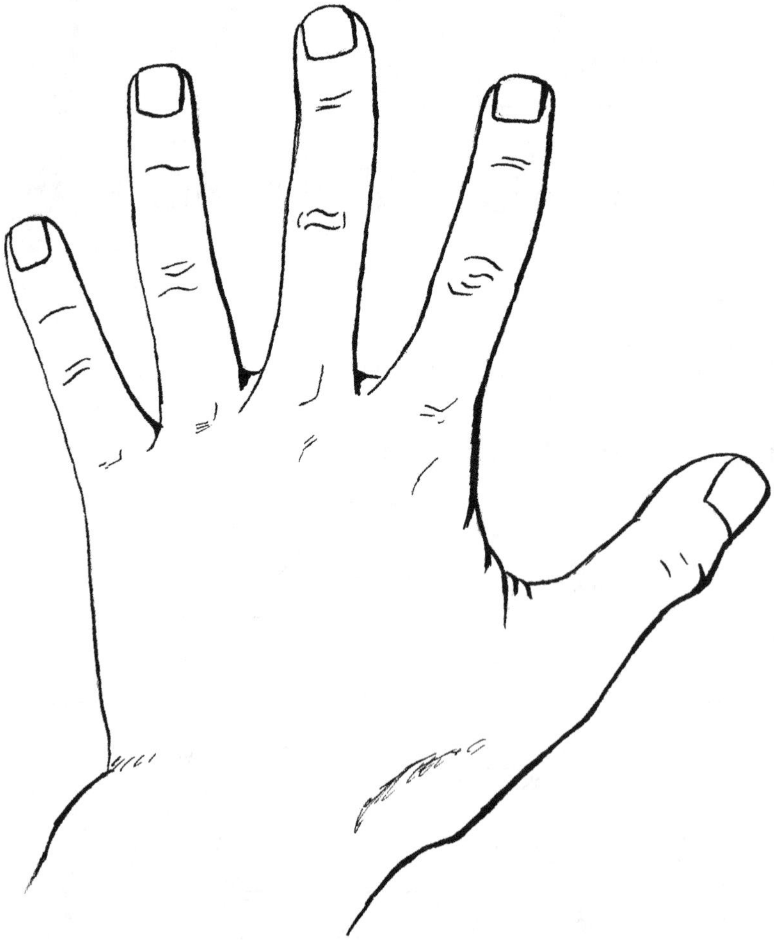

Paul's Second Journey

Acts 15:36-41; 17:1-34

Name ______________________________

Trace the path that Paul and Silas took on their missionary journey. (Their journey began in Antioch of Syria.)

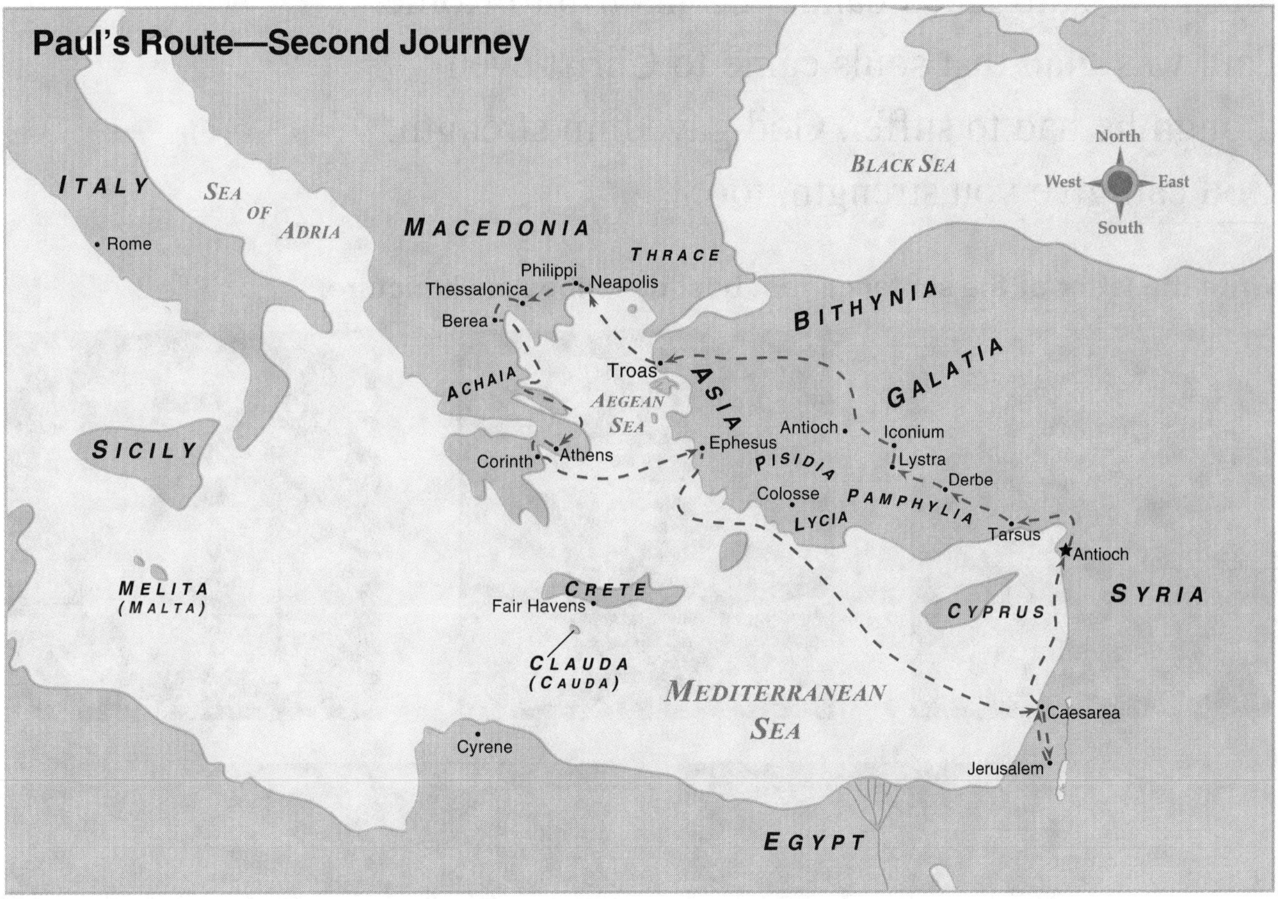

Paul's Route—Second Journey
North
West
East
South
Black Sea
Italy
Sea of Adria
Rome
Macedonia
Thrace
Philippi
Neapolis
Thessalonica
Berea
Bithynia
Troas
Asia
Achaia
Aegean Sea
Galatia
Antioch
Iconium
Lystra
Derbe
Ephesus
Pisidia
Athens
Corinth
Sicily
Colosse
Pamphylia
Lycia
Tarsus
Antioch
Syria
Melita
(Malta)
Crete
Fair Havens
Cyprus
Clauda
(Cauda)
Mediterranean Sea
Caesarea
Jerusalem
Cyrene
Egypt

Write the letter of the correct answer to each question.

_____ 1. Who started on the missionary journey with Paul?

_____ 2. Who told Paul to go preach in Macedonia?

_____ 3. Who joined Paul and Silas on their missionary journey?

_____ 4. Who tried to harm Paul and Silas in Thessalonica?

A. God
B. Silas
C. angry mob
D. Timothy

God Gives Strength

Name ___________________________

Paul faced many dangers on his three missionary journeys. Paul faced danger on his trip to Rome. Paul was glad that souls came to Christ even though he had to suffer. God gave him strength. God can give you strength, too.

Write the letter of the sentence that best describes each picture.

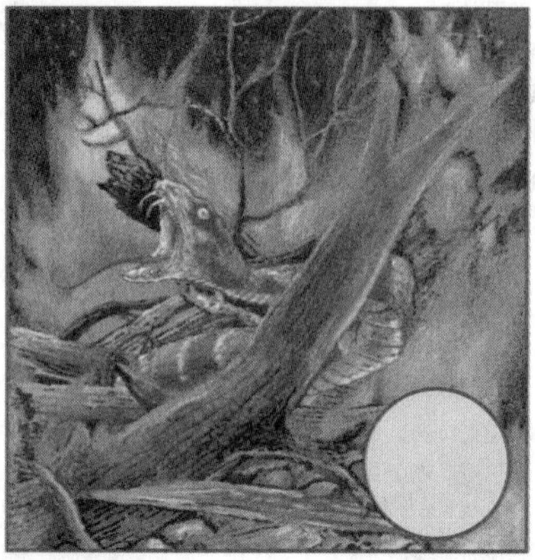

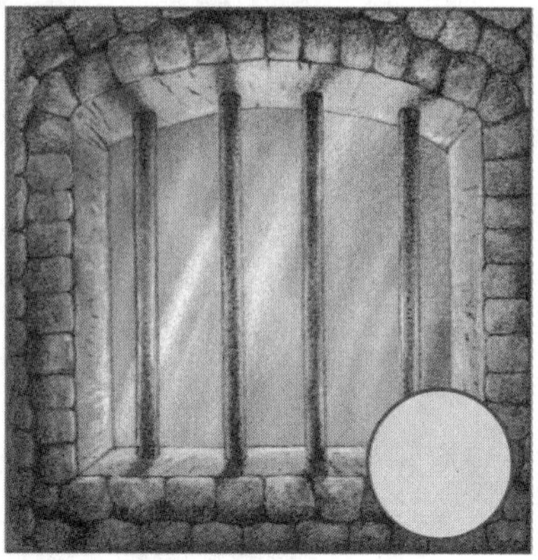

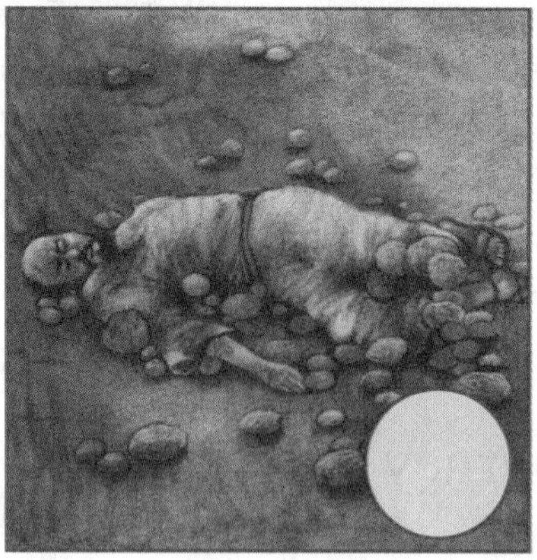

A. Paul was stoned and left for dead (Acts 14:19-20).
B. Paul was placed in prison (Acts 16:22-40).
C. Paul was threatened by angry mobs (Acts 19:29-34).
D. Paul was shipwrecked (Acts 27:39-44).
E. Paul was bitten by a snake (Acts 28:1-6).

Reading from the Bible
Locating Information in a Verse

Name ____________________

When finding a reference in the Bible, remember
- the **title** of the book is at the top of the page
- each **chapter** begins with the word *Chapter*
- every **verse** has a number.

PHILIPPIANS

Chapter 1

Paul and Timotheus, the servants of Jesus Christ, to all the saints in Christ Jesus which are at Philippi, with the bishops and deacons:
2 Grace be unto you, and peace, from God our Father, and from the Lord Jesus Christ.
3 I thank my God upon every remembrance of you,

supply of the Spirit of Jesus Christ,
20 According to my earnest expectation and my hope, that in nothing I shall be ashamed, but that with all boldness, as always, so now also Christ shall be magnified in my body, whether it be by life, or by death.
21 For to me to live is Christ, and to die is gain.

Use the page above to answer the questions.

1. What is the title of this book of the Bible?
   ○ Peter ○ Philippians ○ Galatians

2. What is the number of this chapter?
   ○ 1 ○ 2 ○ 20

Paul started churches in many cities. Paul wrote letters to some of these churches. This book is the letter Paul wrote to the church at Philippi.

Use the verses colored yellow to answer the questions.

3. What is the reference of the verse that tells whom Paul thanked?
   ○ Philippians 1:2 ○ Philippians 1:3

4. Whom did Paul thank? ____________________

Tell Your Friend

Romans 10:14

Name ____________________

You can be a missionary too. You can invite some boys and girls from your neighborhood to go to church with you.

Help Ben talk to his neighbor. Circle one word in each line to write in the speech bubble. Write the word from each line in the numbered spaces to read what Ben said.

1.	P	L	E	A	S	E	V	Y	Q	O	D	I
2.	X	Q	Z	C	O	M	E	M	M	Q	P	R
3.	W	G	T	K	Q	Z	X	X	T	O	Q	Z
4.	S	U	N	D	A	Y	Z	X	Q	B	R	S
5.	T	T	Y	M	S	C	H	O	O	L	X	N
6.	X	W	I	T	H	Q	Z	M	N	L	P	Y
7.	J	Y	T	P	W	Q	Z	T	Q	Z	M	E

Please ______ 1 ______ 2

______ 3 ______ 4 ______ 5

______ 6 ______ 7

God's Word
II Timothy 3:12-17

Name ______________________

Use words from the word bank to finish the puzzle.

1							
2							
3							
4							
5							

believe
book
eternal
inspired
listen

1. God has given us His Word in His special _____.
2. Since God told men what to write, His Word is _____.
3. We must _____ that God's Word is true.
4. We must _____ to what God says to us.
5. God's Word tells us how to have _____ life.

Write the first letter from each word in the puzzle to finish the sentence below.

The B ____ ____ ____ ____ is God's Word.

Our Daily Guide

Name ______________________________

God wants us to read His Word every day.

Make an *X* next to each sentence that tells why we should read our Bibles.

_____ 1. The Bible tells us about God.

_____ 2. The Bible tells us that we are good.

_____ 3. The Bible tells us about our sin.

_____ 4. The Bible helps us with our problems.

_____ 5. The Bible helps us love each other.

Cross out each *A*, *M*, and *S*.

Write the remaining letters in order to make two words that answer the question.

A O S M B S E A M Y M S I A T M

After we read the Bible, what does God want us to do?

___ ___ ___ ___ ___ ___

Good and Useful

II Peter 1:21; II Timothy 3:12-17

Name ______________________________

God wants everyone to be part of His family.
He wants us to grow to be more like Him.

Begin at the star. Connect the dots counting by 5s. Color the picture of what God has given us to help us know about Him.

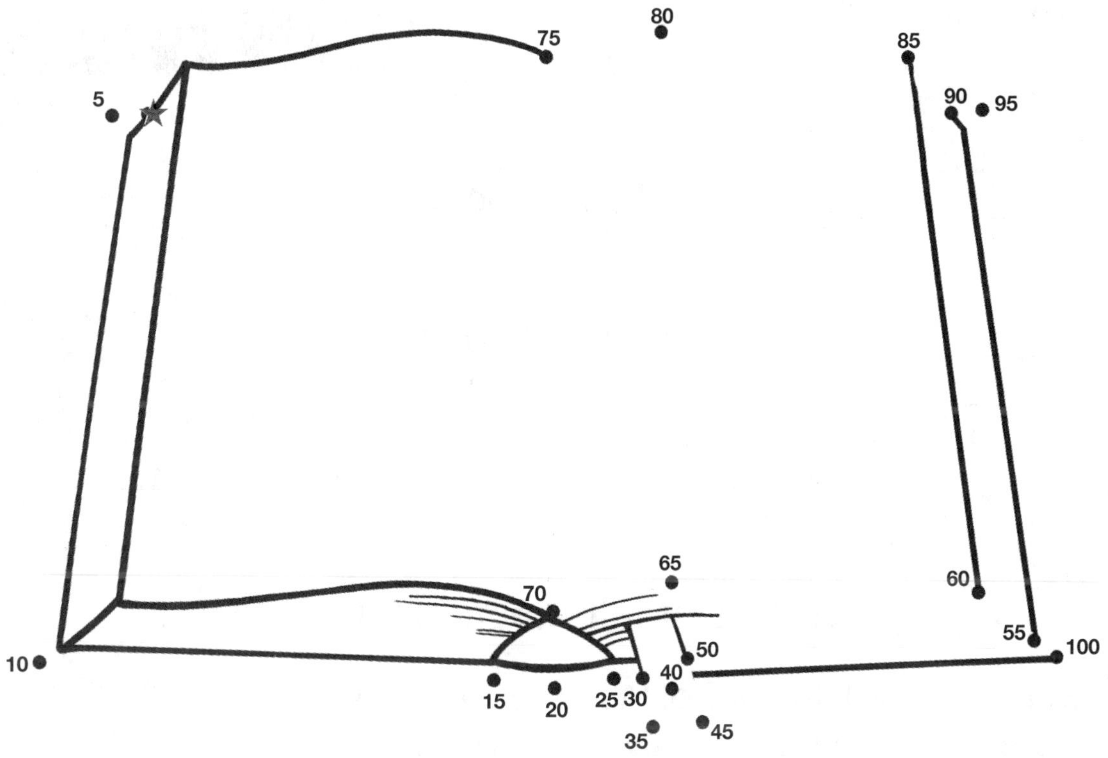

5
10
15
20
25
30
35
40
45
50
55
60
65
70
75
80
85
90
95
100

Write *T* if the sentence is true and *F* if the sentence is false.

_____ 1. The Bible is inspired.

_____ 2. Holy men wrote God's words.

_____ 3. The Bible is good and useful.

_____ 4. The Bible says we will not have problems.

_____ 5. The Bible tells us about salvation.

God's Library

Name ___________________________

The Bible is divided into two main parts. Each part has many books. Many books make a library. Because there are many books in the Bible, we call it God's Library.

OLD TESTAMENT LIBRARY
NEW TESTAMENT LIBRARY
BOOKS OF MOSES
HISTORY
POETRY
MAJOR PROPHETS
MINOR PROPHETS
HISTORY
GENERAL LETTERS
PROPHECY

Write *New* or *Old* to finish each sentence.

The ___________ Testament has 27 books.

The ___________ Testament has 39 books.

The ___________ Testament tells that Christ would come someday.

The ___________ Testament tells about the life of Christ.

Draw a blue box around the three Old Testament pictures.
Draw a red circle around the three New Testament pictures.

God's Word for Me

Name ____________________

God wants us to share His message with others.

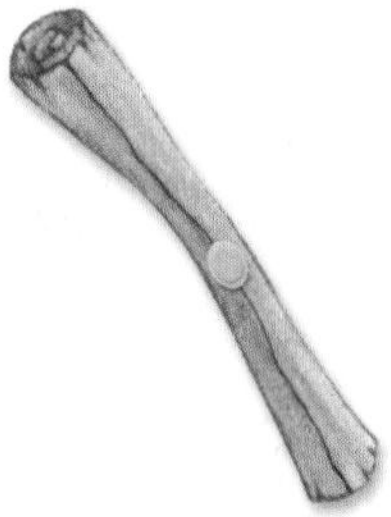

Listen to your teacher read each verse. Write a word from the verse to finish the sentence. Cut out the message. Roll it up like a scroll. Seal your scroll with a sticker. Use your scroll to tell others God's message of love and salvation.

GOD'S MESSAGE for You!

Romans 3:23 God's Word says all have ____________________.

I John 4:14 God sent His ____________________ to die for our sins.

John 3:16 ____________________ loves us and wants us to accept Jesus as our Savior.

Have you accepted Jesus?

God's Word for Me (continued)

Special Treasure

Name ______________________

Treasures are special and are worth a lot to their owners.

What is the greatest treasure that God has given us?

_ _ _ _ _ _ _ _ _ _ _

Fill in the circle next to each reason you should memorize verses.

- ○ to keep God's Word with me
- ○ so I can tell others about God
- ○ I love what they say
- ○ I have to for school
- ○ to please God

Draw a picture of yourself with your special treasure from God.

Obeying God's Word
Nehemiah 8

Name ______________________________

The people of Israel had stopped obeying God. Ezra read God's Word to the people. They were sorry they had not obeyed. Ezra led the people to obey God's Word.

Use the words in the word bank to finish the sentences.

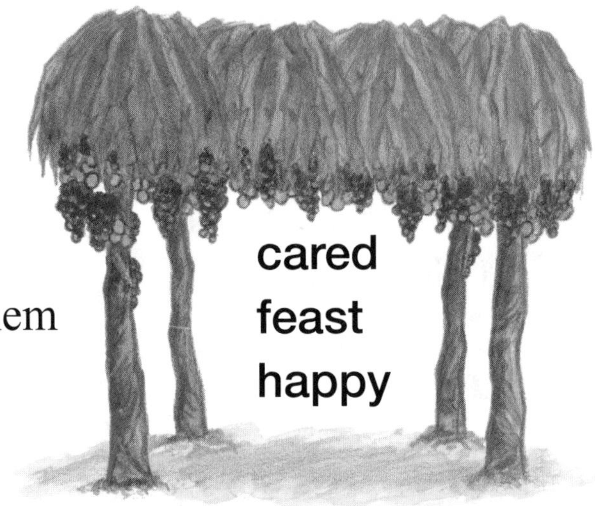

cared
feast
happy

1. The people obeyed God by worshiping Him with a ________________.

2. The feast helped them remember that God ________________ for them in the wilderness.

3. God was ________________ that His people obeyed His Word.

God is happy when I obey His Word.

Finish the sentence with your own words.

I obey God's Word by

____

My Bible, My Guide

Name ______________________

The Bible shows me my sin. The Bible guides me to do right. I can trust God's Word to help me every day.

Lead the boy and girl to the treasure by connecting each good thing the Bible teaches you to do.

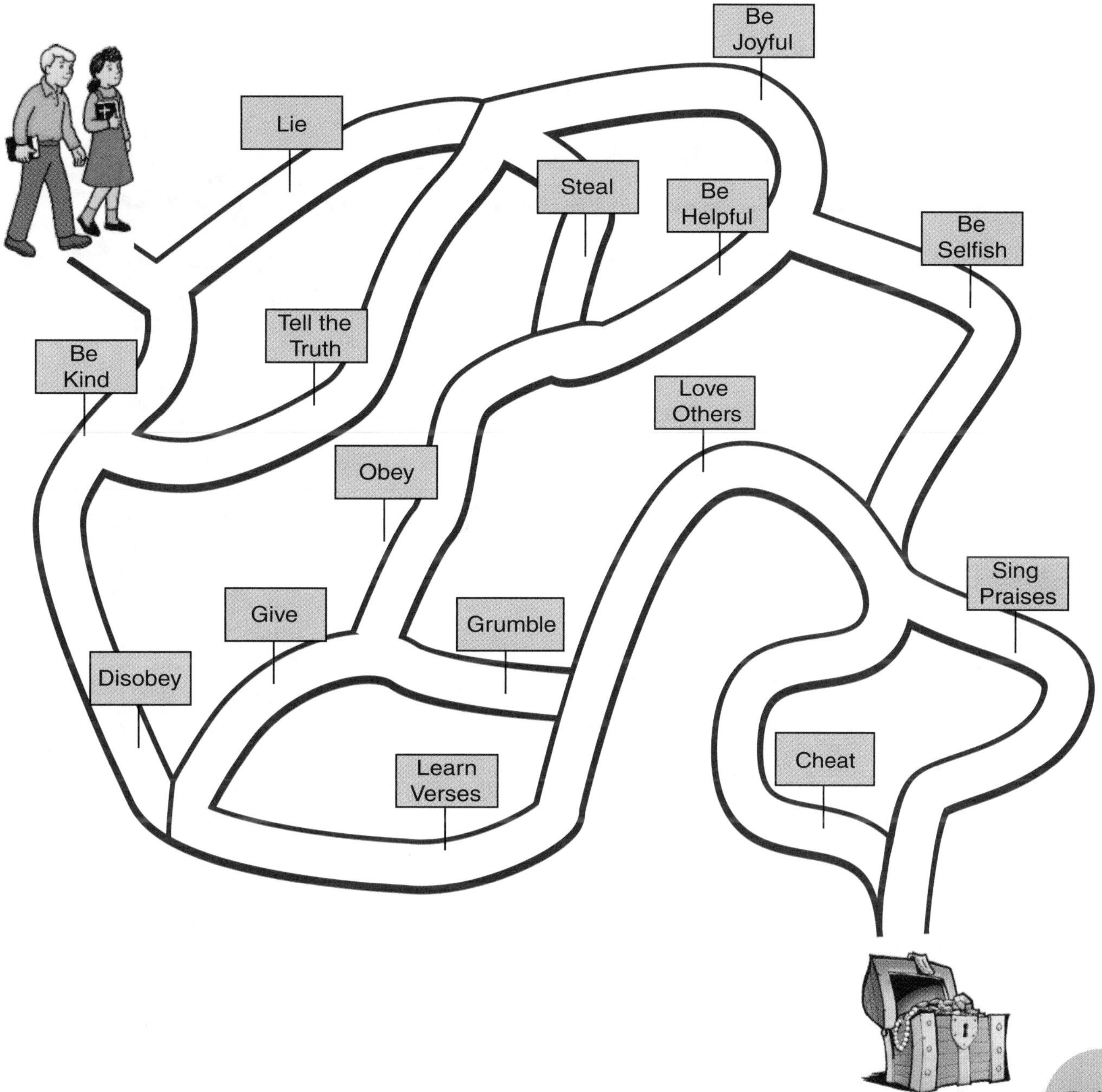

Be Joyful
Lie
Steal
Be Helpful
Be Selfish
Tell the Truth
Be Kind
Love Others
Obey
Sing Praises
Give
Grumble
Disobey
Cheat
Learn Verses

Promises Kept

Name ______________________

God made many promises in the Bible.
God is faithful. God keeps His promises.

Answer the questions.

1. God promised Adam to send a Savior for sin.

   Did God keep His promise? ___________

2. God promised Noah to never again send a flood over the whole earth.

   Has God kept His promise? ___________

3. God promised that His Son would die and rise again to give salvation.

   Did God keep His promise? ___________

4. God promises salvation to those who believe.

   Does God keep His promise? ___________

5. God promises to listen when we pray.

   Does God keep His promise? ___________

Talking with God

Name ______________________

Fill in the circle of each correct answer.

1. Do you talk to your friends and family?

   ○ yes ○ no

2. How often do you talk to your closest friends?

   ○ not very often ○ every chance I get

Jesus is your friend. He died so you could be part of God's family.

3. How does God talk with people?

   ○ on the phone ○ through the Bible

4. How can people talk with God?

   ○ by praying ○ through letters

5. Did Jesus pray?

   ○ yes ○ no

6. Where did Jesus pray?

   ○ only in the temple ○ any place He wanted

7. Can you pray anytime and anywhere?

   ○ yes ○ no

God Is Holy and He Is Able
Matthew 6:9-13

Name ______________________

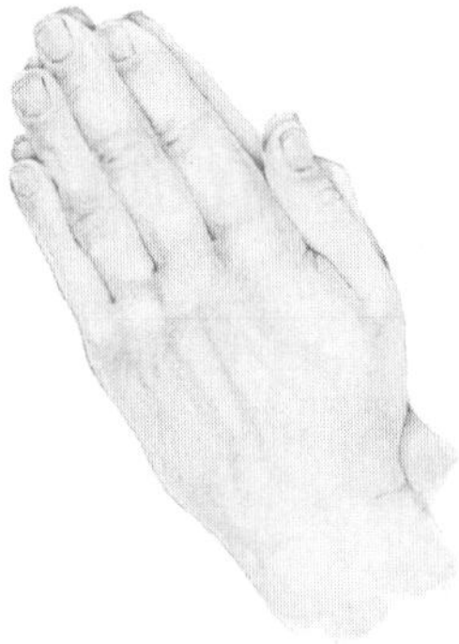

Jesus taught the disciples to honor God as they prayed. The first part of the Lord's Prayer *praises* God for who He is.

Write the letter of the correct word to finish each sentence.

1. God is the heavenly _____ of every Christian.
2. God's _____ is holy.
3. God's _____ and rule is forever.
4. God's plan will be done on _____, just as it is in heaven.

A. kingdom
B. earth
C. Father
D. name

God is able to meet all our needs. Jesus taught the disciples how to ask God for what they needed. The second part of the Lord's Prayer *asks* God to meet our needs.

Write the letter of the correct word to finish each sentence.

5. Please give what we need to live each _____.
6. Please _____ our sins.
7. Please keep us from wanting to _____.
8. Please keep _____ from harming us or helping us sin.

E. forgive
F. day
G. Satan
H. sin

Amen means "let it be so." When you say "Amen" at the end of a prayer, you are agreeing to what was said in the prayer.

God's Men Prayed

Name ____________________

Write the correct names from the word bank to finish the sentences.
Write your name on the last line.

David	Hezekiah	Nehemiah	Daniel	Solomon

God's men prayed; so can I!

1. I can be faithful and pray like D______________ even if others around me do not believe in God.
2. When I am afraid I can remember how King D______________ prayed for courage and safety.
3. Like King S______________ I can thank God for answers to prayer as I claim His promises.
4. When others make fun of me for believing in God, I can remember how God answered the prayer of King H______________.
5. When others are in trouble or in sin, I can remember how n______________ prayed for those he loved.
6. ______________________ can pray anytime and anywhere, and God will hear!

Praising God

Name ______________________________

Choose the picture that matches the sentence.
Write the number of the picture on the line.

_____ I can praise God when I sing.

1

_____ I can praise God when I pray.

2

_____ I can praise God when I give.

3

_____ I can praise God when I play.

4

God Answers Yes

I Kings 18

Name ______________________

Number the pictures in story order.

God soon sent rain to the land.

King Ahab blamed Elijah.

The land was dry from no rain.

The prophets prayed to their gods but no fire came.

King Ahab gathered 850 prophets to meet Elijah.

Elijah prayed and God showed His power with fire.

God Answers No

II Corinthians 12:1-9

Name ______________________________

Do you always get what you want?
Parents sometimes say no.
Teachers sometimes say no.
God sometimes says no.

Fill in the circle next to the best sentence.

The apostle Paul asked God to take away his problem. God told Paul that God's grace would help him with the problem.

○ Paul accepted God's answer and kept serving God with joy.

○ Paul became angry that God did not give him what he wanted.

While shopping with her mom, Wendy looked at the shelves of books. She saw the book her teacher had just finished reading in class. Wendy wanted to buy a copy. Her mom told her that they could borrow one from the library on the way home. What would you do if you were Wendy?

○ I would tell Mom that I need to have the book for my own.

○ I would be glad Mom will take me to the library.

Reading from the Bible
Locating information in a verse

Name ______________________________

The book **title** is at the top of the page.
Each **chapter** begins with the word *Chapter*.
Every **verse** has a number.

I THESSALONIANS

18 Wherefore comfort one another with these
words.

Chapter 5

But of the times and the seasons, brethren,
ye have no need that I write unto you.
2 For yourselves know perfectly that the day
of the Lord so cometh as a thief in the night.

be patient toward all *men.*
15 See that none render evil for evil unto any
man; but ever follow that which is good, both
among yourselves, and to all *men.*
16 Rejoice evermore.
17 Pray without ceasing.
18 In every thing give thanks: for this is the
will of God in Christ Jesus concerning you.

Use the page above to answer the questions.
Fill in the circle next to each correct answer.

1. What is the title of this book of the Bible?

   ○ II Timothy ○ Titus ○ I Thessalonians

2. What is the number of this chapter?

   ○ 5 ○ 1 ○ 18

Use the verses colored yellow to answer the questions.

3. What is the reference of the verse that says we are to "pray without ceasing"?

   ○ I Thessalonians 7:5 ○ I Thessalonians 5:17

4. What does I Thessalonians 5:16 say we are to do evermore?

   ____

My Response

Name ______________________________

God has many lessons for us to learn.
One lesson is to act correctly no matter
how He answers our prayers.

Circle the correct words to finish the sentences.

I prayed for a sunny day to go to the park with friends. God gave me the sunny day.

1. God answered ____.

   yes   no   wait

2. I should ____.

   be thankful

   be sad

I want to tell Grandma about Jesus. I prayed she would visit today. She couldn't come.

3. God answered ____.

   yes   no   wait

4. I should ____.

   pout and complain

   pray she will visit soon

I prayed to get a bike for my birthday. I got a game and some books instead. Mom said I might get a bike for Christmas.

5. God answered ____.

   yes   no   wait

6. I should ____.

   patiently pray

   grumble

BLAM-O!
BLAM-O!
AGES 6-94

I prayed that our family could stay in a motel on vacation. We will stay with Dad's friend instead.

7. God answered ____.

   yes   no   wait

8. I should ____.

   say I don't want to go

   be glad

Happy Rest
Motel

Hymns

This Is My Father's World

Traditional English melody
Adapted by Franklin L. Sheppard

Maltbie D. Babcock

1. This is my Fa - ther's world, And to my lis - tening ears All
na - ture sings, and round me rings The mu - sic of the spheres.
This is my Fa - ther's world: I rest me in the thought Of
rocks and trees, of skies and seas; His hand the won - ders wrought.

2. This is my Father's world,
The birds their carols raise,
The morning light, the lily white,
Declare their Maker's praise.
This is my Father's world:
He shines in all that's fair;
In the rustling grass I hear Him pass,
He speaks to me everywhere.

3. This is my Father's world,
O let me ne'er forget
That though the wrong seems oft so strong,
God is the Ruler yet.
This is my Father's world:
The battle is not done;
Jesus who died shall be satisfied,
And earth and heaven be one.

Anywhere with Jesus

Jessie B. Pounds | Daniel B. Towner

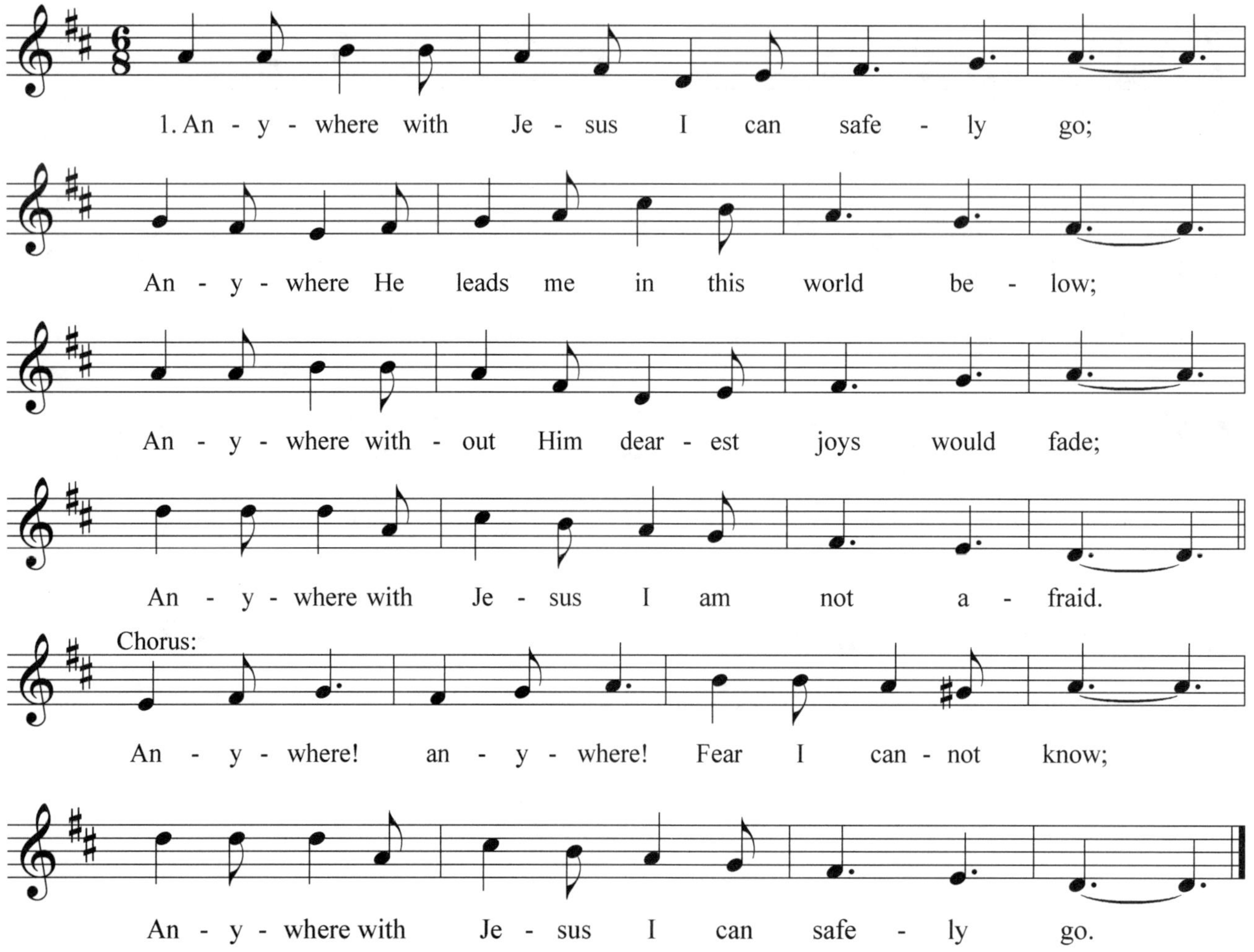
1. An - y - where with Je - sus I can safe - ly go;
An - y - where He leads me in this world be - low;
An - y - where with - out Him dear - est joys would fade;
An - y - where with Je - sus I am not a - fraid.
Chorus:
An - y - where! an - y - where! Fear I can - not know;
An - y - where with Je - sus I can safe - ly go.

2. Anywhere with Jesus I am not alone;
Other friends may fail me, He is still my own;
Though His hand may lead me over dreary ways,
Anywhere with Jesus is a house of praise.
Chorus:
Anywhere! anywhere! Fear I cannot know;
Anywhere with Jesus I can safely go.

3. Anywhere with Jesus I can go to sleep,
When the dark'ning shadows round about me creep;
Knowing I shall waken never more to roam,
Anywhere with Jesus will be home, sweet home.
Chorus:
Anywhere! anywhere! Fear I cannot know;
Anywhere with Jesus I can safely go.

Trust and Obey

John H. Sammis | Daniel B. Towner

1. When we walk with the Lord In the light of His Word What a
glo - ry He sheds on our way! While we do His good will He a -
bides with us still, And with all who will trust and o - bey.
Chorus:
Trust and o - bey, for there's no oth - er way To be
hap - py in Je - sus, But to trust and o - bey.

2. Not a shadow can rise,
Not a cloud in the skies,
But His smile quickly drives it away;
Not a doubt nor a fear,
Not a sigh nor a tear,
Can abide while we trust and obey.
Chorus:
Trust and obey, for there's no other way
To be happy in Jesus,
But to trust and obey.

3. But we never can prove
The delights of His love
Until all on the altar we lay;
For the favor He shows,
And the joy He bestows,
Are for them who will trust and obey.
Chorus:
Trust and obey, for there's no other way
To be happy in Jesus,
But to trust and obey.

4. Then in fellowship sweet
We will sit at His feet,
Or we'll walk by His side in the way;
What He says we will do,
Where He sends we will go;
Never fear, only trust and obey.
Chorus:
Trust and obey, for there's no other way
To be happy in Jesus,
But to trust and obey.

O Come, All Ye Faithful

John F. Wade
Trans. by Frederick Oakeley

John F. Wade's "Cantus Diversi"

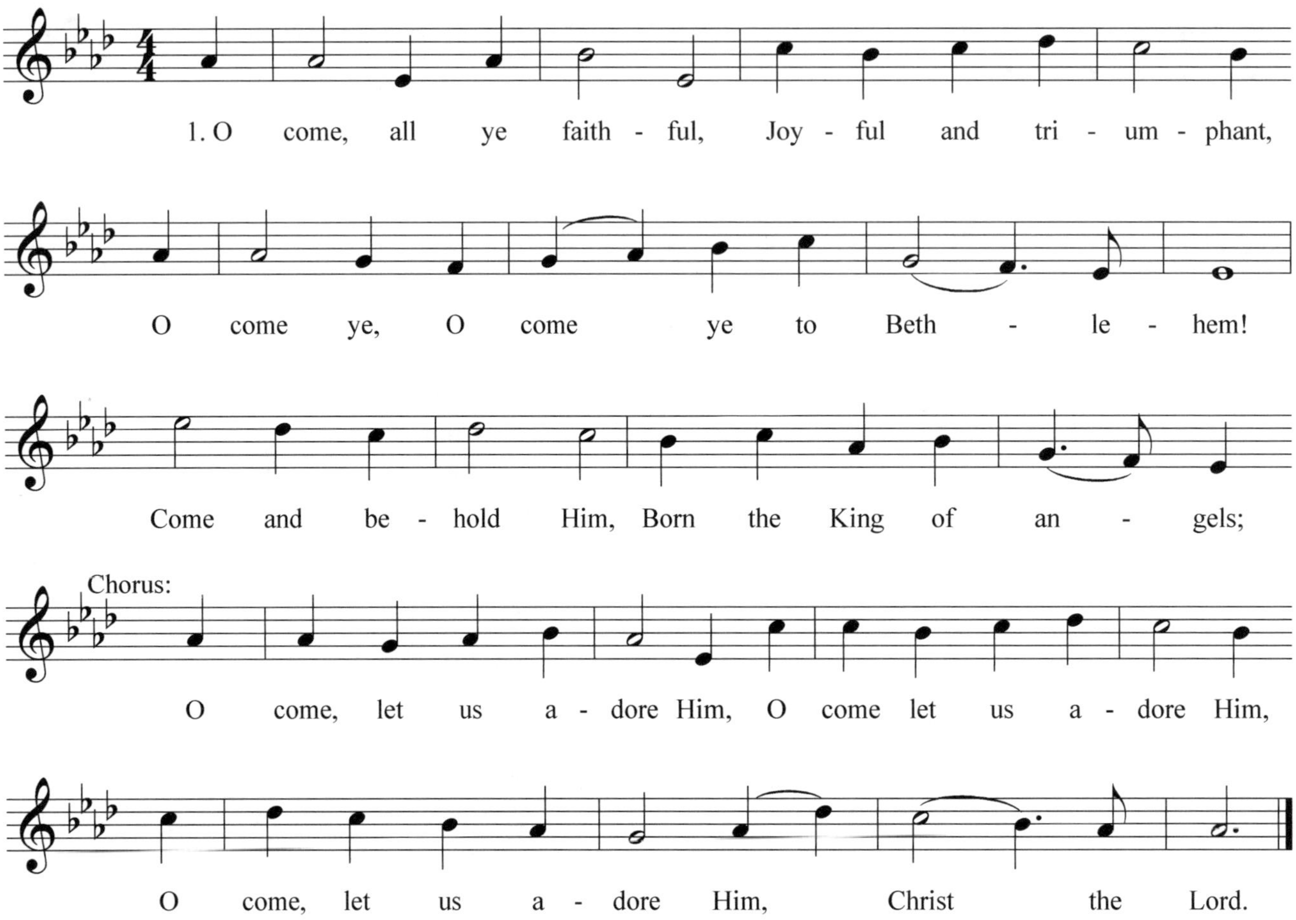
1. O come, all ye faith - ful, Joy - ful and tri - um - phant,
O come ye, O come ye to Beth - le - hem!
Come and be - hold Him, Born the King of an - gels;
Chorus:
O come, let us a - dore Him, O come let us a - dore Him,
O come, let us a - dore Him, Christ the Lord.

2. Sing, choirs of angels,
Sing in exultation!
O sing, all ye bright hosts of heaven above;
Glory to God, all
Glory in the highest;
Chorus:
O come, let us adore Him,
O come, let us adore Him,
O come, let us adore Him,
Christ the Lord.

3. Yea, Lord, we greet Thee,
Born this happy morning,
Jesus, to Thee be all glory given;
Word of the Father,
Now in flesh appearing;
Chorus:
O come, let us adore Him,
O come, let us adore Him,
O come, let us adore Him,
Christ the Lord.

Follow On

William O. Cushing Robert Lowry

1. Down in the val-ley with my Sav - ior I would go, Where the flow'rs are blooming and the
sweet wa - ters flow; Ev - 'ry-where He leads me I would fol - low, fol - low on,
Chorus:
Walk-ing in His foot-steps till the crown be won. Fol-low! fol - low! I would fol-low Je-sus!
An - y - where, ev - 'ry - where, I would fol - low on! Fol - low! fol - low!
I would fol - low Je - sus! Ev - 'ry-where He leads me I would fol - low on!

2. Down in the valley with my Savior I would go,
Where the storms are sweeping and the dark waters flow;
With His hand to lead me I will never, never fear,
Danger cannot fright me if my Lord is near.
Chorus:
Follow! follow! I would follow Jesus!
Anywhere, ev'rywhere, I would follow on!
Follow! follow! I would follow Jesus!
Ev'rywhere He leads me I would follow on!

3. Down in the valley, or upon the mountain steep,
Close beside my Savior would my soul ever keep;
He will lead me safely in the path that He has trod,
Up to where they gather on the hills of God.
Chorus:
Follow! follow! I would follow Jesus!
Anywhere, ev'rywhere, I would follow on!
Follow! follow! I would follow Jesus!
Ev'rywhere He leads me I would follow on!

A Child of the King

Harriet E. Buell

John B. Sumner

1. My Fa - ther is rich in hous - es and lands, He hold - eth the
wealth of the world in His hands! Of ru - bies and dia - monds, of
sil - ver and gold, His cof - fers are full, He has rich - es un - told.
Chorus:
I'm a child of the King, A child of the King: With
Je - sus my Sav - ior, I'm a child of the King.

2. My Father's own Son, the Savior of men,
Once wandered on earth as the poorest of them;
But now He is reigning forever on high,
And will give me a home in heav'n by and by.
Chorus:
I'm a child of the King,
A child of the King:
With Jesus my Savior,
I'm a child of the King.

3. I once was an outcast stranger on earth,
A sinner by choice, and an alien by birth;
But I've been adopted, my name's written down,
An heir to a mansion, a robe, and a crown.
Chorus:
I'm a child of the King,
A child of the King:
With Jesus my Savior,
I'm a child of the King.

4. A tent or a cottage, why should I care?
They're building a palace for me over there;
Tho' exiled from home, yet still I may sing:
All glory to God, I'm a child of the King.
Chorus:
I'm a child of the King,
A child of the King:
With Jesus my Savior,
I'm a child of the King.

Jesus Is All the World to Me

Will L. Thompson

Will L. Thompson

1. Je - sus is all the world to me, My life, my joy, my all;
He is my strength from day to day, With - out Him I would fall.
When I am sad to Him I go, No oth - er one can cheer me so;
When I am sad He makes me glad, He's my Friend.

2. Jesus is all the world to me,
   My Friend in trials sore;
   I go to Him for blessings, and
   He gives them o'er and o'er.
   He sends the sunshine and the rain,
   He sends the harvest's golden grain;
   Sunshine and rain, harvest of grain,
   He's my Friend.

3. Jesus is all the world to me,
   And true to Him I'll be;
   Oh, how could I this Friend deny,
   When He's so true to me?
   Following Him I know I'm right,
   He watches o'er me day and night;
   Following Him, by day and night,
   He's my Friend.

4. Jesus is all the world to me,
   I want no better friend;
   I trust Him now, I'll trust Him when
   Life's fleeting days shall end.
   Beautiful life with such a Friend;
   Beautiful life that has no end;
   Eternal life, eternal joy,
   He's my Friend.

Golden Harps Are Sounding

Frances R. Havergal | Frances R. Havergal

1. Gold - en harps are sound - ing, An - gel voic - es sing,
Gates of pearl are o - pened, O - pened for the King;
Christ the King of glo - ry, Je - sus, King of love,
Is gone up in tri - umph To His throne a - bove.
Chorus:
All His work is end - ed, Joy - ful - ly we sing:
Je - sus hath as - cend - ed! Glo - ry to our King!

2. He who came to save us,
He who bled and died,
Now is crowned with glory
At His Father's side;
Nevermore to suffer,
Nevermore to die,
Jesus, King of glory,
Has gone up on high.
Chorus:
All His work is ended,
Joyfully we sing:
Jesus hath ascended!
Glory to our King!

3. Praying for His children
In that blessed place,
Calling them to glory,
Sending them His grace;
His bright home preparing,
Faithful ones, for you;
Jesus ever liveth,
Ever loveth too.
Chorus:
All His work is ended,
Joyfully we sing:
Jesus hath ascended!
Glory to our King!

O Jesus, I Have Promised

John E. Bode | Arthur H. Mann

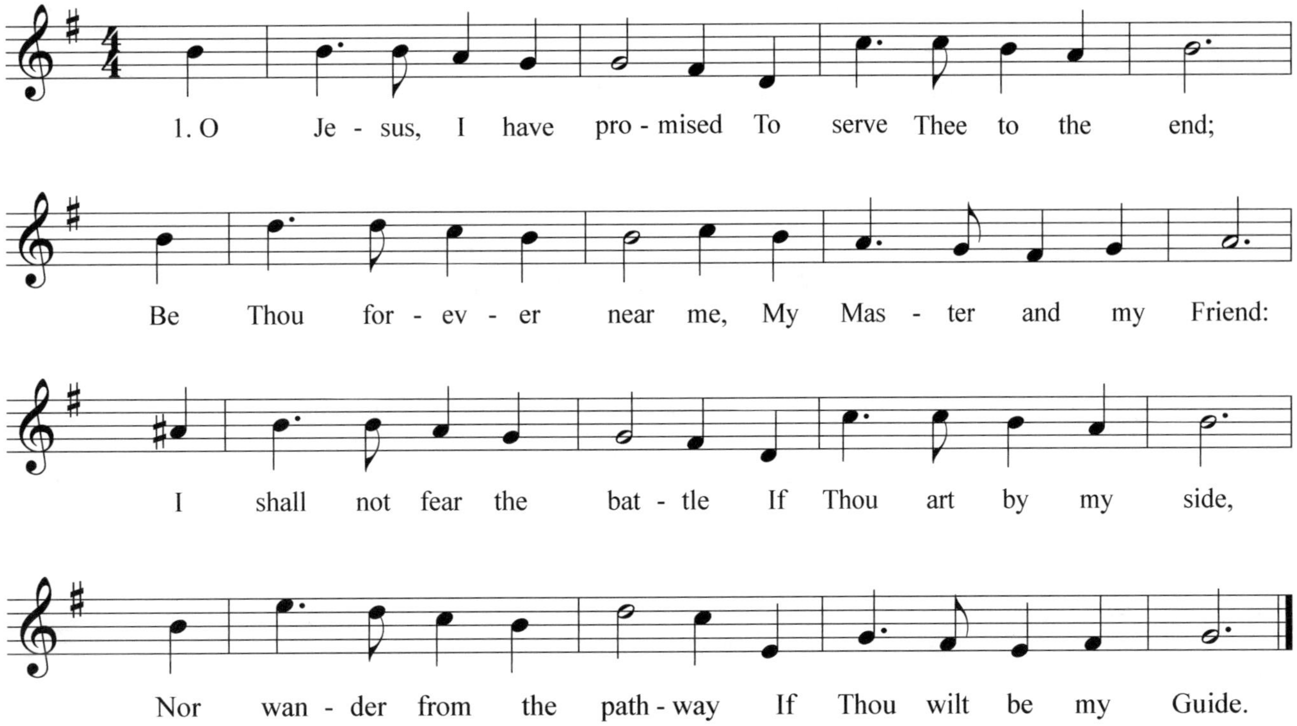
1. O Je - sus, I have pro - mised To serve Thee to the end;
Be Thou for - ev - er near me, My Mas - ter and my Friend:
I shall not fear the bat - tle If Thou art by my side,
Nor wan - der from the path - way If Thou wilt be my Guide.

2. O let me feel Thee near me!
The world is ever near;
I see the sights that dazzle,
The tempting sounds I hear:
My foes are ever near me,
Around me and within;
But, Jesus, draw Thou nearer,
And shield my soul from sin.

3. O Jesus, Thou hast promised
To all who follow Thee,
That where Thou art in glory,
There shall Thy servant be.
And, Jesus, I have promised
To serve Thee to the end;
O give me grace to follow,
My Master and my Friend.

Jesus Loves Even Me

Philip P. Bliss

Philip P. Bliss

1. I am so glad that our Fa - ther in heaven Tells of His love in the
Book He has given; Won - der - ful things in the Bi - ble I see—
This is the dear - est, that Je - sus loves me.
Chorus:
I am so glad that
Je - sus loves me, Je - sus loves me, Je - sus loves me;
I am so glad that Je - sus loves me, Je - sus loves e - ven me.

2. Though I forget Him and wander away,
Still He doth love me wherever I stray;
Back to His dear loving arms would I flee,
When I remember that Jesus loves me.
Chorus:
I am so glad that Jesus loves me,
Jesus loves me,
Jesus loves me;
I am so glad that Jesus loves me,
Jesus loves even me.

3. Oh, if there's only one song I can sing,
When in His beauty I see the great King,
This shall my song in eternity be:
"Oh, what a wonder that Jesus loves me!"
Chorus:
I am so glad that Jesus loves me,
Jesus loves me,
Jesus loves me;
I am so glad that Jesus loves me,
Jesus loves even me.

Bible Land Maps

Map of the Ancient World

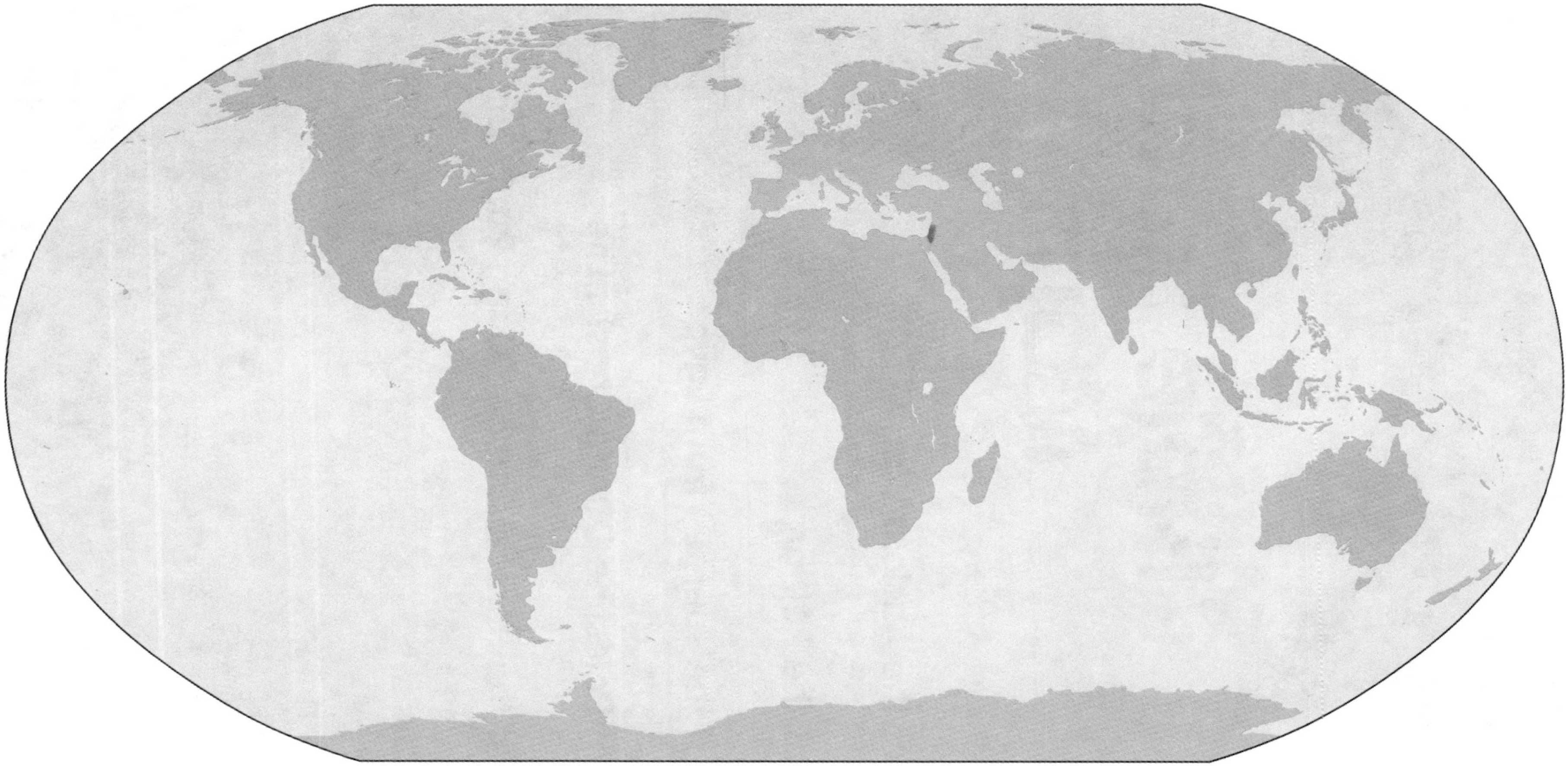

Map of the Patriarchs

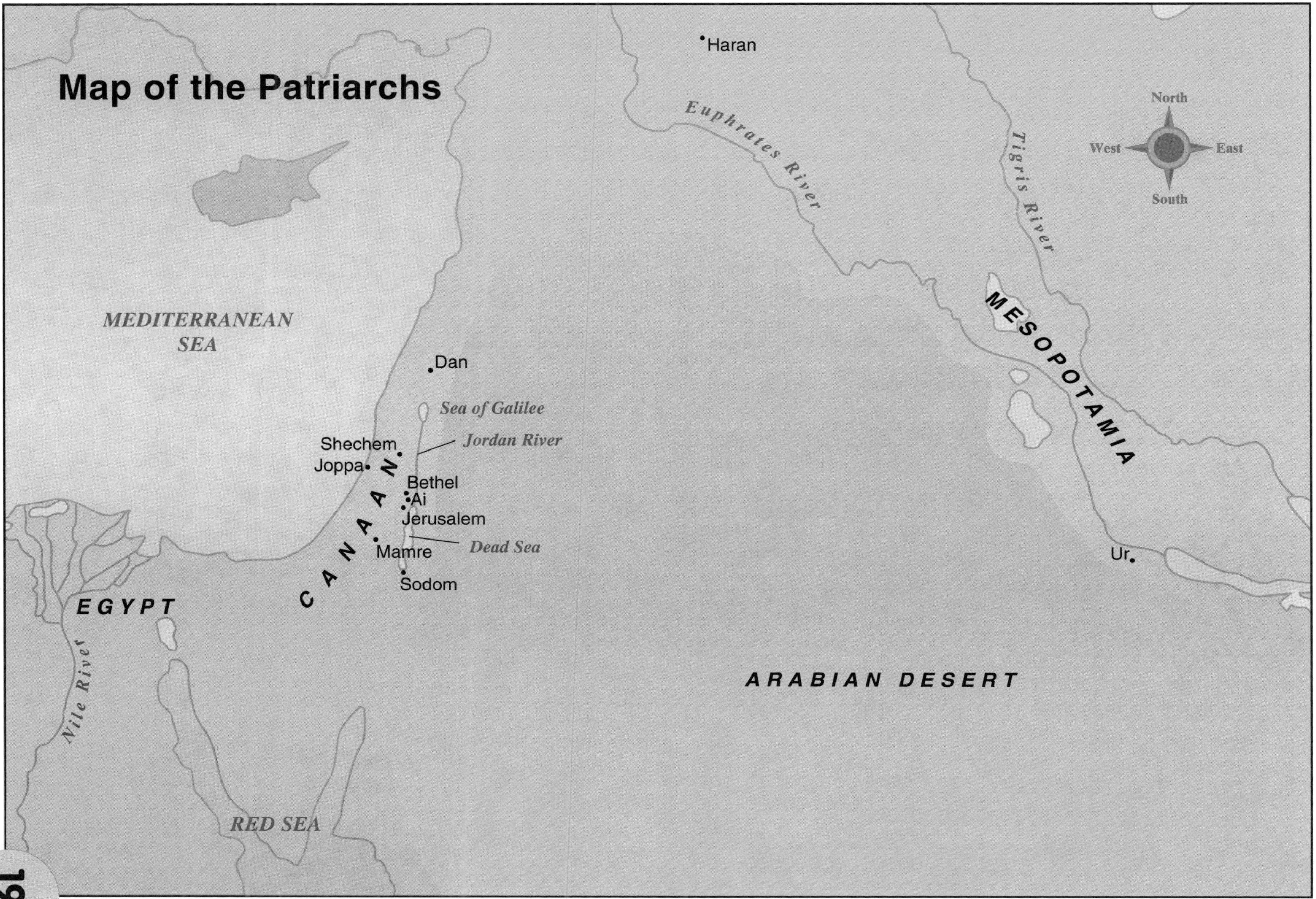
Haran
Euphrates River
Tigris River
North
West
East
South
MESOPOTAMIA
Ur
MEDITERRANEAN SEA
Dan
Sea of Galilee
Jordan River
Shechem
Joppa
Bethel
Ai
Jerusalem
Dead Sea
Mamre
Sodom
CANAAN
EGYPT
Nile River
RED SEA
ARABIAN DESERT

Map of the Journey from Egypt

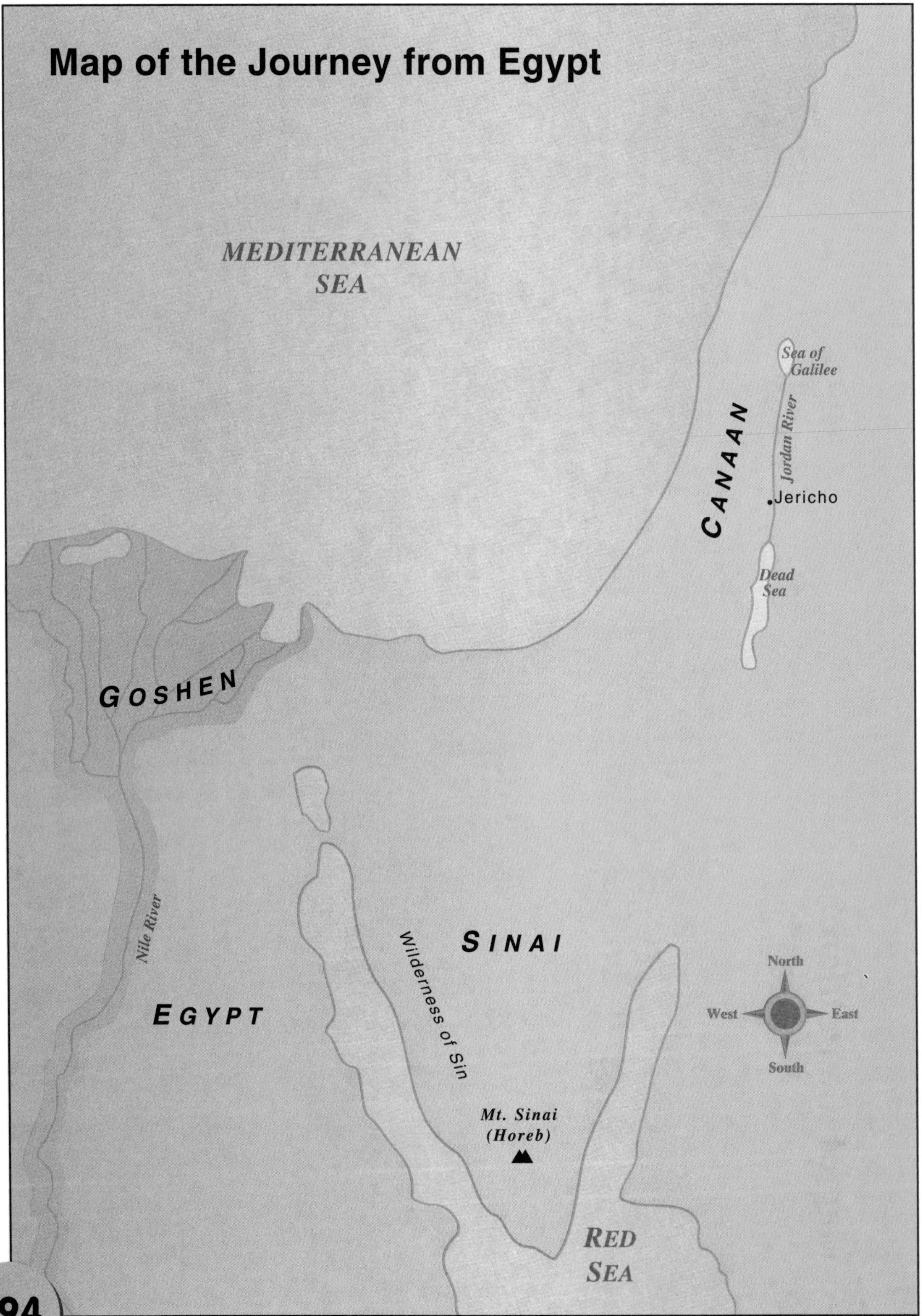
MEDITERRANEAN SEA
Sea of Galilee
Jordan River
CANAAN
Jericho
Dead Sea
GOSHEN
Nile River
SINAI
Wilderness of Sin
EGYPT
North
West
East
South
Mt. Sinai (Horeb)
RED SEA

Map of Palestine During Christ's Life

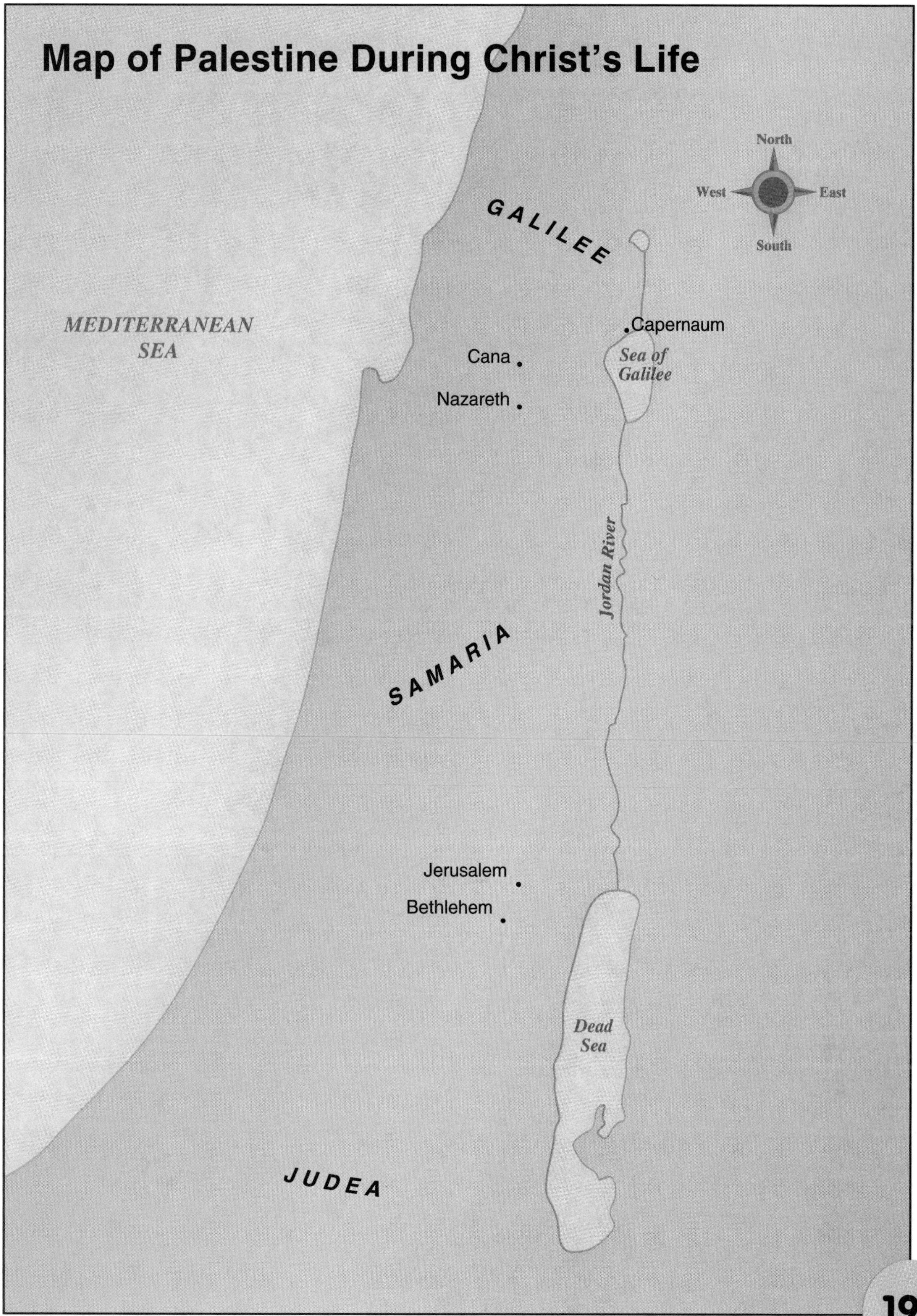
North
West
East
South
GALILEE
MEDITERRANEAN SEA
Capernaum
Cana
Sea of Galilee
Nazareth
Jordan River
SAMARIA
Jerusalem
Bethlehem
Dead Sea
JUDEA

Roman Empire During Paul's Life

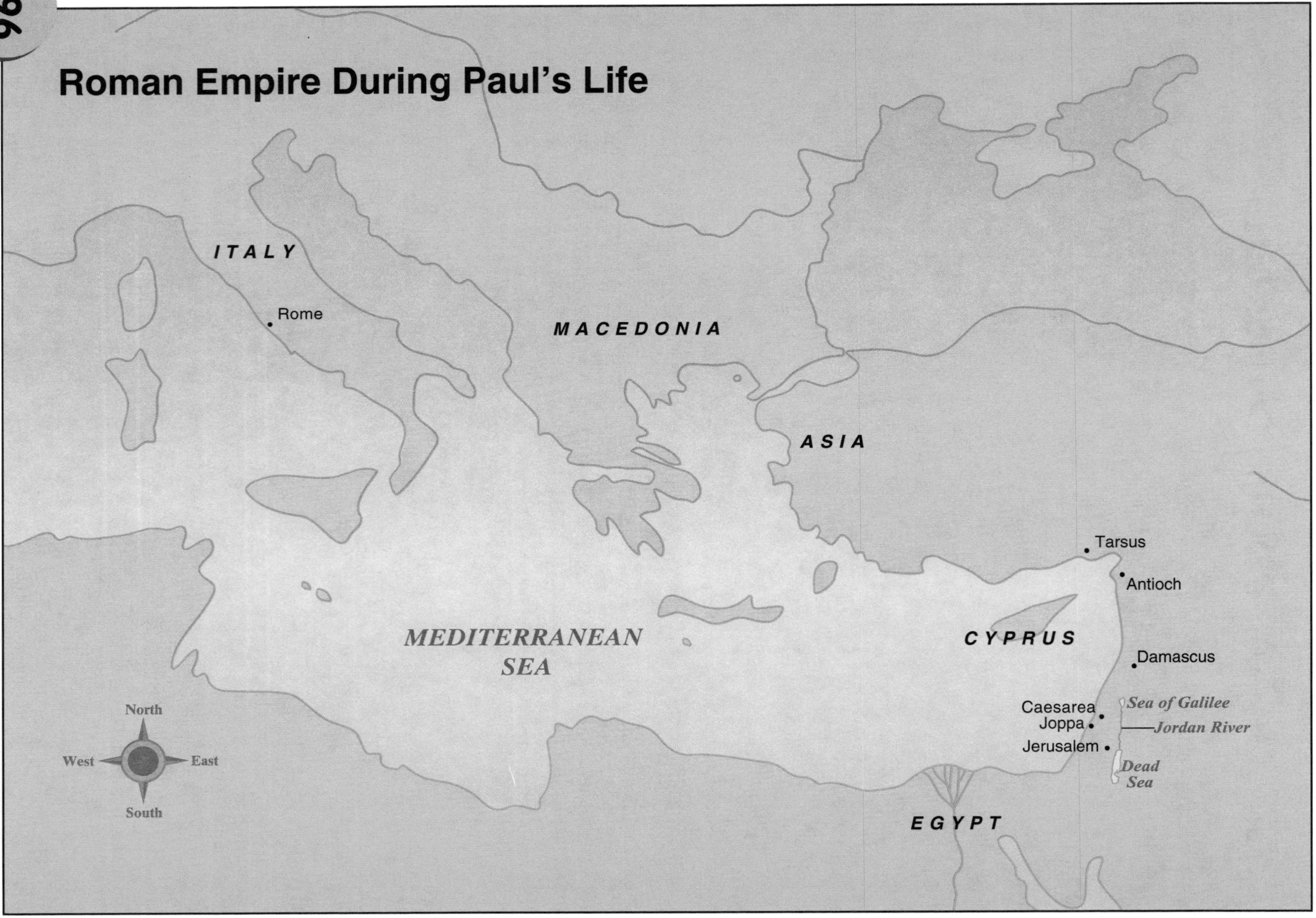
ITALY
Rome
MACEDONIA
ASIA
MEDITERRANEAN SEA
CYPRUS
Tarsus
Antioch
Damascus
Caesarea
Joppa
Jerusalem
Sea of Galilee
Jordan River
Dead Sea
EGYPT
North
South
East
West

Adoniram Judson:

God's Man in Burma

The missionary biography *Adoniram Judson: God's Man in Burma* by Sharon Hambrick is used in teaching lessons in Unit 9. This life story of Adoniram Judson follows him from childhood and youthful unbelief to trust in Jesus Christ and service on the mission field of Burma. This book is written above the first-grade reading level, so the teacher will read the chapters aloud before discussing the story with the students. Worktext pages 197-206 are designed to accompany the teaching of the story.

Adoniram Judson: God's Man in Burma may be purchased through BJU Press. For more information, call 1-800-845-5731 or look for the catalog at www.bjup.com.

Adoniram Judson: God's Man in Burma
Chapters 1-2

Name ______________________________

Adoniram obeyed his parents.
God blessed Adoniram.

Make an *X* under the speaker.

	Mother	Adoniram
1. "I will be very good!"		
2. "I have the most wonderful idea."		
3. "Father said I will be a great man!"		
4. "You must be more humble."		

Circle the best word to finish the sentence.

1. Adoniram learned to read from the _____.

Bible storybook newspaper

2. Adoniram thought he was too _____ to read.

big little cold

3. Adoniram liked to pretend he was a _____.

teacher preacher tiger

4. Adoniram was glad that he had pleased his _____.

sister teacher father

Adoniram Judson: God's Man in Burma
Chapters 3-4

Name ________________________________

God promises to help you.
God always keeps His promises.

What new word is formed from these two pictures?

+
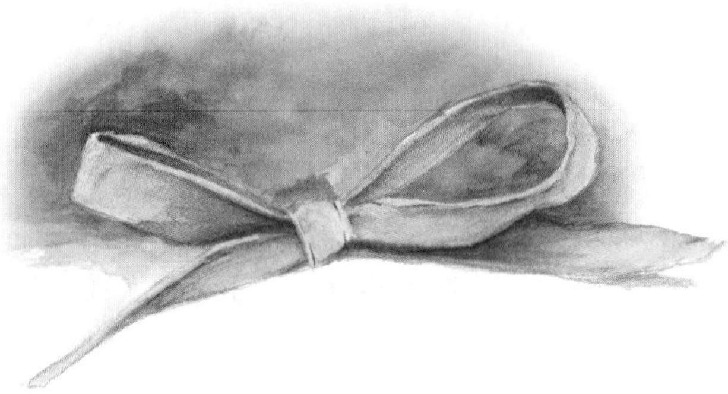

Circle the new word.

raincoat   gift   rainbow

Draw a picture of the new word.

Adoniram Judson: God's Man in Burma
Chapters 5-6

Name ______________________________

Adoniram loved God.
Adoniram wanted to obey God.
He decided to go to another country
to tell people about Jesus.

Circle the correct answer to each question.

1. Who was sad that Adoniram wanted to become a missionary?

2. Who captured Adoniram on his trip to England?

3. What did the American man use to help Adoniram escape from prison?

4. Who encouraged Adoniram to trust in God when he returned to America?

Name ______________________________

Adoniram Judson and his wife Ann traveled far from their home. They went to tell other people about Jesus.

Trace the dotted line from America to Burma.

Color the water 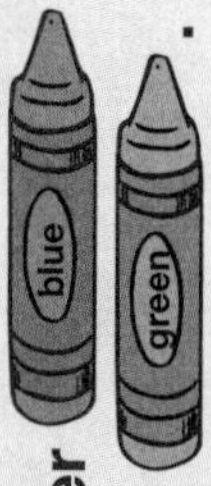 blue
green.

Color the land.

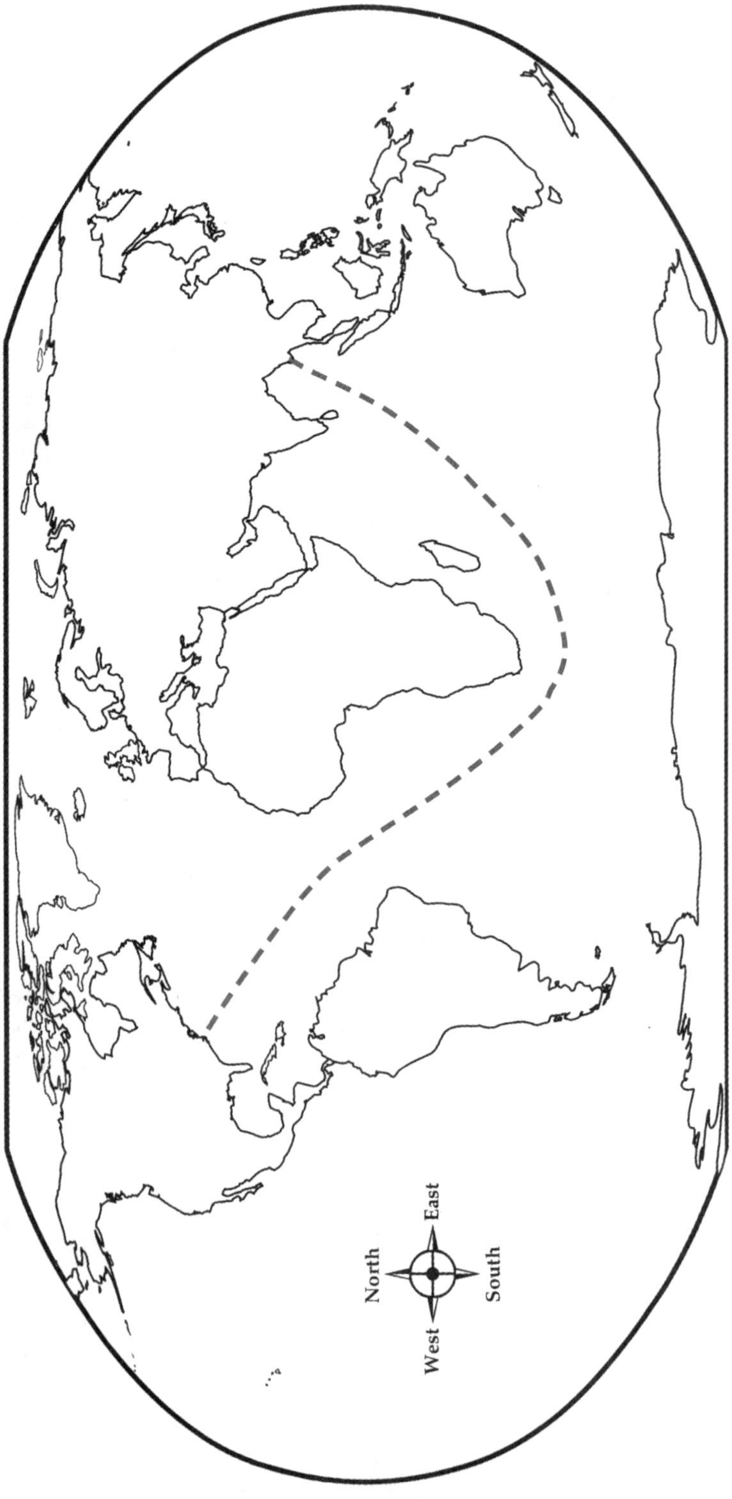
North
East
South
West

Adoniram Judson: God's Man in Burma
Chapter 9

Name ____________________

Adoniram worked hard.
He wanted people to know about Jesus.

Number the events in story order.

Adoniram Judson: God's Man in Burma

Chapters 10-11

Name ______________________________

Adoniram learned to write the Burmese language. He translated God's Word into Burmese.

Use the Burmese letters to find the missing words.

A	G	I	K	N	V

(These Burmese characters do not necessarily correspond with the American alphabet.)

Adoniram and Ann left the city of Rangoon

and moved to ______________________.

Adoniram wanted to tell the

______________________ about Jesus.

Adoniram Judson: God's Man in Burma

Chapters 12-13

Name ______________________________

Adoniram loved God even when he was in a horrible prison.

Fill in the circle next to the correct answer.

1. Some prisoners thought Adoniram was ____.
   - ○ funny
   - ○ crazy
2. Adoniram wanted to be more like ____.
   - ○ the guard
   - ○ Jesus
3. When he was freed from prison, Adoniram ____.
   - ○ preached the gospel
   - ○ went back to America
4. Ann encouraged her husband to ____.
   - ○ trust and obey God
   - ○ be afraid of the king
5. Even when he was sad, Adoniram believed ____.
   - ○ he should quit
   - ○ that God's promises were good

Adoniram Judson: God's Man in Burma
Chapter 14

Name ____________________

Adoniram did not stop serving God.
God blessed Adoniram.

Will you serve God?
Will you tell other people
about Jesus?

Complete the puzzle by using the words in the word bank.

heaven	God	Karen
chief	adventure	bat

Across

2. With _____, nothing is impossible.
4. Adoniram told the people the way to _____.
5. A _____ landed on the lady's hat.
6. Adoniram preached to the _____ people.

Down

1. Adoniram and the Burmese Christians went on an _____.
3. The village _____ believed on Jesus.

1
A
2
D
3
V
4
E
N
5
T
U
6
R
E

Bible Truths for Christian Growth

The list of Bible Truths for Christian Growth provided in this book has been condensed to make it more age-appropriate. A complete list of all the Bible Truths questions and answers may be found on the BJU Press website's product resources page (www.bjupress.com/resources).

Do I Know About God?

1. **Who is God?**
   God is a spirit and does not have a body like man.
   (John 4:24)

2. **What is God like?**
   God is infinite, eternal, and unchangeable.
   (Psalms 139:7-10; 90:2; Malachi 3:6)

3. **Where is God?**
   God is everywhere.
   (Psalm 139:7-12; Proverbs 15:3)

4. **Can you see God?**
   No, I cannot see God, but He always sees me.
   (Jeremiah 23:23-24; John 1:18)

5. **Does God know all things?**
   Yes, nothing can be hidden from God.
   (Job 34:21)

6. **Can God do all things?**
   Yes, God can do all His holy will.
   (Matthew 19:26)

7. **Does God ever do evil?**
   No, God is always good.
   (Exodus 34:6; Psalm 86:5)

8. Are there more gods than one?
No, there is only one God.
(Isaiah 45:6; I Timothy 2:5)

9. In how many persons does this one God exist?
God exists in three persons.
(Matthew 3:16-17; II Corinthians 13:14)

10. Who are the three persons of God?
The three persons of God are the Father, the Son, and the Holy Spirit.
(Matthew 28:19)

11. Who made God?
Nobody made God.
(Psalm 90:2)

12. Has God ever had a beginning?
No, God has always been.
(Psalm 90:2; Revelation 4:8)

13. Will God ever die?
No, God lives forever.
(Psalm 90:2)

14. What is God's attitude toward us?
God loves us unconditionally.
(John 3:16; Romans 5:8)

Do I Know About God's Creation?

1. **Who made you?**
   God made me.
   (Genesis 1:27; Job 33:4)

2. **What else did God make?**
   God made all things.
   (Genesis 1:1-31; John 1:3)

3. **Why did God make you and all things?**
   God made me and all things for His own glory.
   (Romans 11:36; I Corinthians 6:20)

4. **How can you glorify God?**
   I can glorify God by loving Him and doing what He commands.
   (Micah 6:8; I John 5:3)

5. **Why ought you to glorify God?**
   I ought to glorify God because He made me and takes care of me.
   (Psalm 146:5-10)

6. **Where do you learn how to love and obey God?**
   I learn how to love and obey God in the Bible alone.
   (Deuteronomy 30:11-16; Joshua 1:8)

7. **Who wrote the Bible?**
Holy men who were taught by the Holy Spirit wrote the Bible.
(II Peter 1:21)

8. **Who were our first parents?**
Adam and Eve were our first parents.
(Genesis 2:7, 18-22)

9. **Of what were our first parents made?**
God made the body of Adam out of the dust of the ground and formed Eve from the body of Adam.
(Genesis 2:7, 21-22)

10. **Whom did God make Adam to be like?**
God made Adam after His own image.
(Genesis 1:27; 9:6)

11. **What did God give Adam and Eve besides bodies?**
God gave them souls that could never die.
(Genesis 2:7)

12. **Do you have a soul as well as a body?**
Yes, I have a soul that can never die.
(Ecclesiastes 12:7; I Thessalonians 5:23)

13. How do you know that you have a soul?

God tells me so in Genesis 2:7, "And the Lord God formed man of the dust of the ground, and breathed into his nostrils the breath of life; and man became a living soul."

(Genesis 2:7)

14. In what condition did God make Adam and Eve?

God made them holy and happy.

(Genesis 1:27-31)

Do I Know What God Says About Sin?

1. **What is a covenant?**
   A covenant is an agreement between two or more persons.
   (Genesis 9:11-17)

2. **What was Adam's part in the covenant in order to stay in the Garden of Eden?**
   Adam was required to obey God perfectly.
   (Genesis 2:15-17)

3. **Did Adam obey God?**
   No, Adam chose to disobey God.
   (Genesis 3:6)

4. **Did Adam's sin affect himself alone?**
   No, Adam's sin made all men lose communion with God and become sinful in nature and subject to God's wrath.
   (Romans 5:14; 6:23; Ephesians 2:3)

5. **How did God punish Adam's disobedience?**
   Adam's punishment was death and separation from God.
   (Genesis 3:17-24)

6. **What is sin?**
   Sin is the transgression of the law of God.
   (I John 3:4)

7. **What is meant by transgression?**
Transgression is failing to do what God commands or doing what God forbids.
(Psalm 25:6-7; Matthew 15:3-6)

8. **What was the sin of our first parents?**
Adam and Eve disobeyed God and ate the fruit that God told them not to eat.
(Genesis 2:17; 3:6)

9. **Who tempted Adam and Eve to sin?**
Satan tempted Eve, and she gave the fruit to Adam.
(Genesis 3:1-6)

10. **What happened to our first parents when they had sinned?**
Instead of being holy and happy, they became sinful and miserable.
(Genesis 3:8-24)

11. **What effect did Adam's sin have on all mankind?**
Because of Adam's sin, every man is born with a sinful nature that wants to do evil and has no fellowship with God.
(Romans 5:12)

12. What is that sinful nature we inherit from Adam called?

Our corrupt nature is called original sin.

(Psalm 51:5; Romans 5:12)

13. What does every sin deserve?

Every sin deserves the wrath and curse of God.

(Psalm 89:30-32; Galatians 3:10)

Do I Know About the Work of Christ?

1. Who can save us?

The only Savior of men is the Lord Jesus Christ.

(John 14:6; Acts 4:12)

2. What does God require of man before he can go to heaven?

No one can enter heaven unless his heart is changed.

(John 3:3, 16; Acts 4:12)

3. What is this change of heart called?

This change of heart is called regeneration.

(Ezekiel 36:26-27; Titus 3:5-6)

4. Who can change a sinner's heart?

The Holy Spirit can change a sinner's heart.

(Titus 3:5)

5. How is a heart changed?

A heart is changed by the Holy Spirit because of the grace of God shown in the work of Christ.

(Titus 3:4-7)

6. What is grace?

Grace is God's kindness to us when we deserve punishment.

(Deuteronomy 7:6-9; Ephesians 2:8-9)

7. **What is the work of Christ?**
The work of Christ is to keep perfectly the law of God and to suffer the penalty for our sins.
(II Corinthians 5:21; Hebrews 9:11-14)

8. **Can anyone be saved by his own works?**
No one can be saved by his own works.
(Ephesians 2:8-9; Titus 3:4-7)

9. **Did Christ ever sin?**
No, Christ was holy, sinless, and undefiled.
(II Corinthians 5:21; Hebrews 7:26)

10. **How could the Son of God suffer?**
Christ, the Son of God, became man that He might obey and suffer in our nature.
(Philippians 2:7-8; Hebrews 2:9)

11. **What is meant by atonement?**
The atonement is Christ's satisfying divine justice by His sufferings and death in the place of sinners.
(Romans 5:8-11)

12. **What do we gain from the work of Christ?**
God regenerates, justifies, and sanctifies those who believe in Christ.
(I Corinthians 6:11; Titus 3:5-7)

13. What is justification?

Justification is God's forgiving me and treating me just as if I had never sinned.

(Romans 3:24-25; II Corinthians 5:19, 21)

14. How am I justified?

I am justified by faith in the work of Christ and on the grounds of His righteousness.

(Romans 3:25-28)

15. What is sanctification?

Sanctification is God's making me holy in heart and behavior.

(I Corinthians 6:19-20)

16. What are the two parts of sanctification?

The two parts of sanctification are dying to sin and living to righteousness.

(Romans 8:13; Galatians 2:20)

17. For whom did Christ obey and suffer?

Christ obeyed and suffered for sinners.

(Romans 5:8)

18. What kind of death did Christ die?

Christ died the painful and shameful death of being nailed to a cross.

(Luke 23:33-38; Philippians 2:8)

19. Who will be saved?

Whoever repents and believes on the Lord Jesus Christ will be saved.

(Isaiah 55:7; John 3:16)

20. What does it mean to repent?

To repent is to be sorry for sin and to hate and forsake it because it is displeasing to God.

(II Chronicles 7:14; II Corinthians 7:9)

21. What is saving faith in Christ?

Saving faith is believing that Christ died for my sins, that He was buried, and that He rose again according to the Scriptures.

(I Corinthians 15:1-4)

22. Can you repent and believe in Christ by your own power?

No, I cannot repent and believe in Christ without the help of God's Holy Spirit.

(John 3:5-6; Titus 3:5)

23. Does Christ care for little children?

Yes, for He says in Mark 10:14, "Suffer the little children to come unto me, and forbid them not: for of such is the kingdom of God."

(Mark 10:14)

24. How long has it been since Christ died?
Christ died nearly 2,000 years ago.

25. How were people saved before the coming of Christ?
People were saved by believing in a Savior to come.
(Hebrews 11:13)

26. How did people show their faith before the coming of Christ?
People showed their faith by offering sacrifices on God's altar.
(Hebrews 11:4)

27. What did the sacrifices represent?
The sacrifices represented Christ, the Lamb of God, who was to die for sinners.
(John 1:29, 36; Hebrews 9:11-14)

28. How many offices does Christ have?
Christ has three offices.
(Acts 3:22; Hebrews 5:5-6; Revelation 19:16)

29. What are Christ's offices?
Christ's offices are prophet, priest, and king.
(Acts 3:22; Hebrews 5:5-6; Revelation 19:16)

30. How is Christ a prophet?
Christ teaches us the will of God.
(Luke 4:18; John 15:15)

31. How is Christ a priest?

Christ died for our sins and pleads with God for us.

(Romans 3:26; Hebrews 7:25-27)

32. How is Christ a king?

Christ rules over us, defends us, and will establish His kingdom on earth.

(Isaiah 33:22; I Corinthians 15:25)

A

almighty all-powerful; one of God's names

angel heavenly messenger sent by God to earth; spirit who lives with God in heaven

apostle man chosen by Jesus to see the events of His life and His Resurrection and to tell others of Him

ark large boat built by Noah

ark of the covenant the sacred box in which the Ten Commandments, a pot of manna, and Aaron's rod were kept

ascension Christ's going upward into heaven forty days after His Resurrection

assurance condition of knowing for sure; certainty

atone to give a satisfactory payment for a sin, wrongdoing, or injury

B

baptize to wash with water as a sign of a believer's following after Christ

begotten being the child of

beseech to beg or plead with

blessed holy; having God's favor

blessing a gift from God

born again referring to one who has experienced the new birth (See *new birth.*)

Bread of Heaven a name for Christ, who provides physical and spiritual food

burnt offering Old Testament offering to God that was burned on an altar

C

caesar a title given to Roman emperors

Calvary "the place of a skull"; the place near Jerusalem where Jesus was crucified; Golgotha

Canaan the land that God promised to give to the Israelites in the Old Testament; a name symbolizing heaven

centurion Roman commander of about one hundred soldiers

charity love

cherubim more than one angel of the class called cherubs

Christian a person who believes in and accepts Christ as his Savior

church all of those who believe in Christ and are saved

cleanseth frees from guilt; purges or clears

Comforter the Holy Spirit

commandment an order

commend to give to someone for safekeeping

condemn to declare guilty of wrongdoing

confess to admit to doing wrong; to admit one's guilt; saying what God says about sin

corrupt evil and dirty; wicked; sinful

countenance expression of a person's face; the face itself

covenant promise or agreement made between two or more persons

create to make something from nothing

creator one that makes something new; Creator God

crucify to put to death by nailing or binding to a cross

D

Day of Atonement a day once a year when the high priest entered the holy of holies to offer sacrifices as payment for the people's sins

death separation of the body and spirit; separation from God

demon an evil spirit

descend to come down; to pass down from parent to child

devil an evil spirit; a demon; another name for Satan

disciple one who follows and serves Jesus; a follower of a certain belief

divine having to do with God; holy and sacred

doctrine what a certain group of people believes and teaches; a belief or principle

draught drawing in of fish in a net

E

edify to build up spiritually

Elohim a Hebrew name for God indicating His power and authority

Emmanuel a name of Jesus, meaning "God with us"

epistle letter or written work

eternity time without beginning or end

eunuch man in charge of a royal household

evangelize to spread the gospel

everlasting without end; going on forever

exalt to speak highly of; to praise and glorify

exhort to try to convince

F

faith trust in God; firm belief without physical proof

false prophet man who preaches or teaches religious ideas against those found in God's Word; deceiver

fellowship being together as friends; enjoying each other's company

firmament sky between the heavens and the earth

fisher of men person who leads others to be saved

follower one who serves another; one who believes and lives by another's teachings; disciple

forerunner person who goes before to prepare the way for another or to tell of another's coming

foretold predicted; told about future happenings

forgiveness act of excusing or pardoning someone for a wrongdoing

fornication immoral or evil behavior; idolatry

frankincense gum from certain trees that gives off a spicy, sweet odor when burned

fruit anything yielded or produced

G

genealogy record of ancestral descent; family tree

generation all the people born in a certain time period

Gentile any person who is not Jewish

girdle belt worn at the waist around a loose fitting thigh-length shirt

glorify to praise or worship

Good Shepherd a name for Christ showing He leads and guides us

gospel the truth of the good news of Christ's coming to earth, dying for our sins, and rising from the tomb

grace God's kindness to us even though we do not deserve it

Great Commission Christ's command to His disciples to teach the gospel (Matthew 28:19-20)

guilty having done wrong and deserving punishment

H

harlot bad or immoral woman

heart innermost center of the natural condition of man; center of man's thought life and emotions

heathen person who does not know of or believe in God

heaven glorious and happy place where God and His angels live; where saved people will live eternally

Hebrew Jewish language; Jewish person

hell place of dreadful and endless torment where the unsaved are punished after death

high priest head or chief of the Jewish priests with the responsibility of overseeing the temple and administering religious ceremonies

holy attribute of God: sinless, perfect, and righteous

holy of holies the holiest place; place in the tabernacle where the ark of the covenant was kept

Holy Spirit the third Person of the Trinity who lives in the hearts of Christians; the Holy Ghost

homage special respect shown to honor someone

honor *n.* glory and praise; honesty; *vb.* to treat with love, admiration, and respect

household of faith believers born into the family of God through faith in Jesus Christ; born-again Christians

humble not proud of oneself or boastful; meek or modest

humility state of being without self-pride and boastfulness

I

I Am one of the names for God showing His eternal existence "apart from" creation

idol statue worshiped as a god; person or thing loved more than God

image likeness; something that is like another in form or nature; idol

impute to transfer (righteousness or guilt) from one person to another

incarnate the Son of God in human flesh

incense substance that gives off a sweet smell when it is burned

incorruptible clean and perfect; without error

infinite very great; without boundary; endless

iniquity sin and wickedness

inspiration God's breathing (of the Scriptures) into holy men

intercede to plead on behalf of another

Israel God's chosen people; the Jews; the land of the Jews

J

Jehovah the personal name of God in the Old Testament, meaning "the Eternal One who reveals Himself"

Jew a person of the Hebrew race, God's chosen people

Jubilee Year a celebration the Jews observed every fifty years

judgment act of hearing and deciding a case; decision given by a judge

just right, fair, and honest; good and righteous

justify to declare righteous

L

Lamb name used for Jesus Christ; it shows that by His death He paid the sacrifice for our sins just as a lamb was sacrificed in the Old Testament for the sins of the Israelites

laver large bowl used in washing sacrifices in the Jewish tabernacle or temple

law rule made by God or human authority

leaven substance such as yeast that causes dough to rise; often considered a symbol of sin in the Bible

leper person who has leprosy

leprosy skin disease that attacks the nerves, causes weakening and wasting away of muscles, and is characterized by white, scaly scabs; a picture of sin

Levite member of the tribe of Levi from which the Jewish priests were chosen

longsuffering patience in pain or trouble

Lord God; Jesus Christ

Lord's Supper communion; a church service by which we remember Christ's sacrifice on the cross; the last meal that Jesus had with His disciples

lots (to cast) using bits of paper or wood to decide the outcome or determine the portion of something given to each person

Lucifer Satan's name before he was cast out of heaven

M

magistrate officer of a government, such as a judge or president

malefactor one who does evil; criminal

Man of Sorrows a name for Jesus, showing His sorrow and suffering for the sins of the world

mediator person who acts as a go-between

mercy God's witholding of the punishment we deserve

mercy seat the gold plate covering the ark of the covenant on which the high priest sprinkled the blood for a sin offering; the throne of God

Messiah the Old Testament name for the promised Redeemer; Christ

might power

Millennium period of one thousand years on earth following the Tribulation when Christ will reign

millstone one of two round, flat stones used for grinding grain

miracle supernatural event done by the power of God that shows His works

missionary person who goes out to tell the story of Jesus and God's plan of salvation

moneychanger person who exchanges one kind of money for another kind

myrrh fragrant extract from the wood and bark of a common Palestinian bush

N

Nazarene a person from Nazareth; another name for Jesus

Nazarite a Hebrew who had taken certain religious vows; he could not drink wine, cut his hair, or touch an unclean thing

new birth occasion, upon confession and belief in the gospel, that God gives eternal life to a sinner

new heaven and new earth future heaven and earth that will be created by God

O

obey to do what one is told to do

observance act of keeping customs, laws, or religious ceremonies

offering giving of something as an act of worship to God

omnipotent all-powerful; almighty

omnipresent always present; existing everywhere at the same time

omniscient all-knowing; having complete knowledge of everything

ordinance rule, especially one given by God; a way of remembering Christ's death and Resurrection

P

palsy loss of power to feel or move

parable short story that teaches a lesson; earthly story with a heavenly meaning

paradise heaven; dwelling place of God and His angels, and where the saved will dwell in eternity

pardon forgiveness

Passover the death angel's passing over the Hebrew homes that had blood sprinkled on the doorpost (Exodus 12:13)

Passover Feast an eight-day Jewish feast in remembrance of the Israelites' escape from Egypt

patriarch father, ruler, or founder of a family, tribe, or group

Pentecost a Jewish celebration (feast) held fifty days after Passover to remember the harvest and the giving of the Ten Commandments; the giving of the Holy Spirit to the apostles and early Christians

pharaoh title given to the kings of ancient Egypt

Pharisee member of a Jewish group that was strict in keeping Jewish law

Philistines enemies of the Jews who lived in the Holy Land during Old Testament times

plague suffering or trouble sent from God; rapid spreading of a deadly disease

potter's field cemetery for poor or friendless people

praise to express the worth or value of something through words or songs

prayer act of speaking to God

priest Old Testament servant of God chosen by God to offer sacrifices

proclaim to make known to the public

prodigal wasteful and careless

prophesy to tell about future events; to proclaim God's will

prophet a Bible preacher who told of God's will and future events

propitiation act of appeasing wrath; our means of salvation through Christ's death

proud feeling pleased over something done, made, or owned; honored; dignified

providence divine acts of God in making all things to work out His purpose and plan

province section of a kingdom or an empire; in Roman times, a section of the empire ruled by a governor

psalm religious song, poem, or hymn of praise to God

publican tax collector of ancient Rome

R

rabbi "teacher" or "master"; a Jewish religious leader

ram's horn trumpet made of a curly horn from a male sheep

ransom price paid to free captives

Rapture taking of the saved to heaven when Christ returns

reconcile to bring together again in peace and friendship after being separated

redeemer one who buys back something that was lost; one who saves or sets free; Jesus Christ

redemption act of being rescued or freed from sin; our salvation

regeneration act of receiving a new spiritual life; salvation; new birth

remission forgiveness of sin

repent to be sorry for and ask forgiveness for sin

repentance act of being sorry for, asking forgiveness for, and turning away from sin, or a change of mind about sin

resurrection act of coming to life again

righteous doing that which is right in the sight of God; hating sin and loving good

S

Sabbath the seventh day of the week; the biblical day used for worship and rest

sackcloth rough cloth made from the hair of goats and camels and worn as a sign of sadness

sacrifice offering to God for the forgiveness of sin

Sadducees group of Jews who did not believe in angels or resurrection

saint person who is saved

salvation God's saving us from the punishment of sin

sanctification making holy in heart and behavior by God and the Holy Spirit after salvation

sanctuary holy place set apart for the worship of God

Sanhedrin the Jews' seventy-member supreme court for religious and government cases

Satan another name for the Devil; an evil spirit who is the enemy of God and of all Christians

saved description of one who has believed the gospel and asked forgiveness for sins; set free from sin and its results

savior one who saves others from trouble or disaster

Savior Jesus Christ our Lord

scapegoat one who takes the blame for others; in Old Testament times a goat was taken into the wilderness every year, symbolically taking the blame for the sins of the people; Jesus took the blame for our sins

Scripture holy writings of God; the Bible

separation being set apart; living differently from the unsaved in a total and noticeable way

sepulchre or **sepulcher** tomb or cave used for burial

seraph angel of important position described in Isaiah 6:2 as having six wings and believed to lead in the worship of God

servant person who works for someone else

Sheol a Hebrew name for hell

shofar or **shophar** ancient Hebrew trumpet made of a ram's horn and used for giving signals

sin disobedience to the law of God

slothful lazy

smite to hit or slap; to destroy or kill

sojourn to stay in one place for a time

soothsayer one who tells the future, or pretends to; a fortuneteller

sorcerer person who practices magic and claims to have the help of evil spirits

soul part of the person that thinks, acts, feels, and lives forever

sow to spread or plant seed

surety person who agrees to be responsible for the debts or faults of another

swaddling clothes strips of cloth used to wrap around a newborn baby

synagogue Jewish congregation or a place to meet for worship

T

tabernacle tent used by the Israelites as a place of worship while they were wandering in the wilderness

tablet small flat sheet of stone used for writing

talent unit of weight for gold or silver; ability to do something well

tares harmful weeds that grow in grain fields

temple building used for the worship of God or of false gods

temptation act of trying to make a person do something wrong; attraction

Ten Commandments the ten rules for living that God gave to Moses on Mt. Sinai (Exodus 20)

testament will or promise; divisions of the Bible

testify to give evidence for; to tell about what one has seen or heard

testimony open statement of one's beliefs or faith in God

thresh to separate the grain or seeds from a plant such as wheat

till to plow or cultivate the ground

tithe small part; small tax; offering to God of one-tenth of all that a person earns

transfiguration the changed appearance of Christ on the mountain (Matthew 17:1-13)

transform to change the appearance, shape, or nature of a thing

transgression sin; act of doing what God forbids

translate to take to heaven without death; to make something understandable in another language

trespass to disobey; to sin

tribe any one of the twelve groups of the Hebrews, each of which descended from one of the sons of Jacob

tribute tax; expression of thanks or respect

Trinity God the Father, God the Son, and God the Holy Spirit in one divine nature

trust *n.* firm, unchanging belief in the power, love, or truthfulness of a person or thing; faith and confidence; *vb.* to have faith in

twinkling quick wink of the eye; very short time; moment

U

unbelief lack of thinking that something is true

undefiled clean and pure; not corrupted or made dirty

unfaithful not keeping one's promises

ungodly sinful and wicked

unrighteousness wickedness; sinfulness

V

vainglory great pride in oneself; boastful display or "showing off"; arrogance; opposite of humility

vengeance punishment or injury in return for a wrong

vessel large boat or ship; container for holding liquids; person made or used for some purpose

viper type of poisonous snake

virgin pure, unmarried female

W

watchtower high tower or high place from which to watch for enemy ships, forces, etc.

wayside side of a path or road

wilderness region of land with no people; dry, bare land

wise men men who gain knowledge, especially from the heavens; the men who followed the star from the East to Bethlehem where Jesus was born

witness *n.* person who tells about an event he has seen; *vb.* to tell others about Christ and the way of salvation

Word the way God speaks to man; in Scripture, referring to both the Bible (the written Word) and Jesus Christ (the living Word)

worship to show honor, love, and respect

Y

yoke wooden frame that fastens two oxen or horses together for pulling a plow or heavy load; a burden

Z

Zion heaven; a name for Jerusalem; a hill in Jerusalem that represents the whole city

Index

Illustration Credits

The following individuals have contributed to the illustrations included in this textbook.

Illustrators
Preston Gravely Jr.
Dyke Habegger
Kathy Pflug
David Schuppert
Lynda Slattery
Del Thompson

Contributing Illustrators
Julie Arsenault
Tim Banks
Matt Bjerk
Paula Cheadle
Johanna Ehnis
Justin Gerard
Corey Godbey
Jim Hargis
Jonathan Johnson
Chris Koelle
Joel Leineweber
Mary Ann Lumm
Will Meadows
John Muessen
Keith Neely
Duane Nichols
Asher Parris
John Roberts
Melissa Smith
Ali Teeter
Sanela Tutaris
Yoo Kyung Julie Yang

Photograph Credits

The following agencies and individuals have furnished materials to meet the photographic needs of this textbook. We wish to express our gratitude to them for their important contribution.

1999-2001 www.arttoday.com
Digital Stock
Joyce Landis
Tara Swaney
Wendy Searles
Dawn Watkins
Dr. Stewart Custer
PhotoDisc, Inc.
Unusual Films

Cover
Dawn Watkins

Title Page and Back Cover
PhotoDisc, Inc.

Unit 1
PhotoDisc, Inc. 5 (all), 7 (all top row, 2nd and 4th on bottom row); 1999-2001 www.arttoday.com 7 (1st and 3rd on bottom row)

Unit 2
PhotoDisc, Inc. 32; Joyce Landis 34

Unit 3
Joyce Landis 43 (top and bottom left), 46, 52 (top); Tara Swaney 43 (bottom right), 52 (bottom); Wendy Searles 43 (top right); Digital Stock 44 (all)

Unit 4
PhotoDisc, Inc. 66

Unit 5
PhotoDisc, Inc. 76, 86, 92; Dr. Stewart Custer 83

Unit 6
PhotoDisc, Inc. 109, 110; Dr. Stewart Custer 112

Unit 7
Dr. Stewart Custer 115; Tara Swaney 131; Digital Stock 132

Unit 8
PhotoDisc, Inc. 134 (all except hymnal), 138 (second from bottom and bottom), 141, 142 (background); Joyce Landis 134 (hymnal), 138 (second and third from top); Tara Swaney 138 (top)

Unit 9
Tara Swaney 147, 151; PhotoDisc, Inc. 155

Unit 10
Tara Swaney 162 (left, middle right), 174 (top); Joyce Landis 162 (middle left, right), 174 (middle both); Unusual Films 174 (bottom)

Prayer Journal

PRAYER JOURNAL

PRAYER JOURNAL

PRAYER JOURNAL

PRAYER JOURNAL

PRAYER JOURNAL